Lionel Carley.
Northampton –
November 1970.

THE BLUE BIRD

THE BLUE BIRD

A FAIRY PLAY IN SIX ACTS

by

MAURICE MAETERLINCK

TRANSLATED BY
ALEXANDER TEIXEIRA DE MATTOS

WITH SIXTEEN ILLUSTRATIONS IN COLOUR
BY E. CAYLEY ROBINSON

METHUEN & CO. LTD. LONDON
36 Essex Street W.C.

First Published (Fcap. 8vo), March 25th 1909 ; Second and Third Editions (Fcap. 8vo), 1909 ; Fourth Edition (Paper Covers), December 8th 1909 ; Fifth, Sixth and Seventh Editions (Paper Covers), 1909 ; Eighth Edition (Fcap. 8vo), January 1910 ; Ninth, Tenth, Eleventh and Twelfth Editions (Paper Covers), 1910 ; Thirteenth Edition (Fcap. 8vo), 1910 ; Fourteenth, Fifteenth and Sixteenth Editions (Paper Covers), 1910 ; Seventeenth Edition (Paper Covers with an Additional Act), December 1910 ; Eighteenth Edition (Fcap. 8vo), 1910 ; Nineteenth Edition (Paper Covers), 1911 ; Twentieth Edition (Fcap. 8vo), 1911 ; Twenty-first Edition (Paper Covers), 1911 ; Twenty-second Edition (Cheap Form), October 5th 1911 ; Twenty-third Edition (Cheap Form), 1911 ; Twenty-fourth Edition (Crown 4to, Illustrated), October 12th 1911 ; Twenty-fifth Edition (Illustrated), 1911 ; Twenty-sixth and Twenty-seventh Editions (Cheap Form), 1911 ; Twenty-eighth, Twenty-ninth and Thirtieth Editions (Cheap Form), 1912 ; Thirty-first Edition (Fcap. 8vo), 1912 ; Thirty-second Edition (Illustrated), 1912 ; Thirty-third Edition (Cheap Form), 1913 ; Thirty-fourth and Thirty-fifth Editions (Cheap Form), 1914 ; Thirty-sixth Edition (Cheap Form), 1915 ; Thirty-seventh and Thirty-eight Editions (Cheap Form), 1916 ; Thirty-ninth Edition (Fcap. 8vo), 1917 ; Fortieth Edition (Cheap Form), 1917 ; Forty-first Edition (Cheap Form), 1919 ; Forty-second Edition (Fcap. 8vo), 1919 ; Forty-third Edition (Cheap Form), 1919 ; Forty-fourth Edition (Cheap Form), 1921 ; Forty-fifth Edition (Fcap. 8vo), 1921 ; Forty-sixth Edition (Cheap Form), 1922 ; Forty-seventh Edition (Crown 8vo), 1923 ; Forty-eighth Edition (Illustrated), 1923 ; Forty-ninth and Cheaper Edition (Fcap. 8vo), 1924 ; Fiftieth Edition (Methuen's Modern Classics), 1925 ; Fifty-first Edition (Fcap. 8vo, Cheap Form), 1925 ; Fifty-second Edition (Fcap. 8vo, Cheap Form), 1927 ; Fifty-third Edition (Fcap. 8vo), 1928 ; Fifty-fourth Edition (Methuen's Modern Classics), 1928 ; Fifty-fifth Edition (Methuen's Modern Classics), 1929 ; Fifty-sixth Edition (Fcap. 8vo), 1929 ; Fifty-seventh Edition (Methuen's Modern Classics), 1931 ; Fifty-eighth Edition (Methuen's Modern Classics), 1933 ; Fifty-ninth Edition (F'cap 8vo, Cheap Form), 1934 ; Sixtieth Edition (Methuen's Modern Classics), 1935 ; Sixty-first Edition (Small F'cap 4to, Illustrated), 1936

ILLUSTRATIONS

I

CHARACTERS

(in the order in which they appear upon the scene)

MUMMY TYL

DADDY TYL

TYLTYL

MYTYL

THE FAIRY BÉRYLUNE

THE HOURS

BREAD

FIRE

THE DOG

THE CAT

WATER

MILK

SUGAR

LIGHT

GRANNY TYL

GAFFER TYL

PIERROT

ROBERT

JEAN

MADELEINE

PIERRETTE

PAULINE

RIQUETTE

NIGHT

SLEEP

DEATH

THE GHOSTS

COLD-IN-THE-HEAD

THE WARS

THE SHADES

THE TERRORS

THE STARS

THE PERFUMES OF THE NIGHT

THE WILL-O'-THE-WISPS

THE FIREFLIES

DEW

THE SONG OF THE NIGHTINGALES

THE POPLAR

THE OAK

THE FIR-TREE

THE BEECH

THE ELM

THE LIME-TREE

THE BIRCH

2

THE WILLOW
THE CYPRESS
THE CHESTNUT-TREE
THE OAKLING
THE RABBIT
THE HORSE
THE BULL
THE OX
THE COW
THE WOLF
THE SHEEP
THE PIG
THE COCK
THE GOAT
THE ASS
THE BEAR
THE IVY
THE LUXURY OF BEING RICH
THE LUXURY OF BEING A LANDOWNER
THE LUXURY OF SATISFIED VANITY
THE LUXURY OF DRINKING WHEN YOU ARE NOT THIRSTY
THE LUXURY OF EATING WHEN YOU ARE NOT HUNGRY

THE LUXURY OF KNOWING NOTHING
THE LUXURY OF UNDERSTANDING NOTHING
THE LUXURY OF DOING NOTHING
THE LUXURY OF SLEEPING MORE THAN NECESSARY
FAT LAUGHTER
THE LUXURY OF SHAME
THE FEMALE SLAVES
THE CHILDREN'S HAPPINESS
THE HAPPINESS OF BEING WELL
THE HAPPINESS OF PURE AIR
THE HAPPINESS OF LOVING ONE'S PARENTS
THE HAPPINESS OF THE BLUE SKY
THE HAPPINESS OF THE FOREST
THE HAPPINESS OF SUNNY HOURS
THE HAPPINESS OF SPRING
THE HAPPINESS OF THE SUNSETS
THE HAPPINESS OF SEEING THE STARS RISE

COSTUMES

TYLTYL.—The dress of Hop-o'-my-Thumb in Perrault's Tales. Scarlet knickerbockers, pale-blue jacket, white stockings, tan shoes.

MYTYL.—The dress of Gretel or Little Red Riding-hood.

THE FAIRY BÉRYLUNE and NEIGHBOUR BERLINGOT.— The traditional dress of the poor women in fairy-tales. If desired, the transformation of the Fairy into a princess in Act I may be omitted.

LIGHT.—A moon-coloured dress, that is to say, pale gold shot with silver, shimmering gauzes, forming rays, etc. Neo-Grecian or Anglo-Grecian (à *la* Walter Crane) or even more or less Empire style : a high waist, bare arms, etc. Head-dress : a sort of diadem or even a light crown.

THE DOG.—Red dress-coat, white breeches, top-boots, a shiny hat ; a costume more or less suggesting that of John Bull.

THE CAT.—Black silk tights and spangles.

N.B.—The heads of the DOG and the CAT should be only discreetly animalized.

BREAD.—A rich pasha's dress. An ample crimson silk or velvet gown, embroidered with gold. A huge turban. A scimitar. An enormous stomach, red face and puffed-out cheeks.

SUGAR.—A silk gown, cut like that of a eunuch in a seraglio, half blue and half white, to suggest the paper wrapper of a sugar-loaf. Eunuch's head-dress.

FIRE.—Red tights, a vermilion cloak with changing reflections, lined with gold. An aigrette of iridescent flames.

WATER.—A pale-blue or bluish green dress, with transparent reflections and effects of rippling or trickling gauze. Neo-Grecian or Anglo-Grecian style, but fuller and more voluminous than that of LIGHT. Head-dress of aquatic flowers and seaweed or reeds.

DADDY TYL, MUMMY TYL, GAFFER TYL and GRANNY TYL.—The traditional costume of the German woodcutters and peasants in Grimm's Tales.

TYLTYL'S BROTHERS AND SISTERS.—Different variations of the Hop-o'-my-Thumb costume.

NIGHT.—Ample black garments, covered with mysterious stars and "shot" with reddish-brown reflections. Veils, dark poppies, etc.

THE ANIMALS.—Popular or peasant costumes.

THE TREES.—Dresses of different shades of green or the colour of the trunks of trees. Distinctive attributes in the shape of leaves or branches by which they can be recognized.

THE LUXURIES.—Before the transformation : wide, heavy mantles in red and yellow brocade ; enormous fat jewels, etc. After the transformation : chocolate or coffee-coloured tights, giving the impression of unadorned dancing-jacks.

THE HAPPINESS OF THE HOME.—Dresses of various colours, or, if preferred, costumes of peasants, shepherds, wood-cutters and so on, but idealized and interpreted fairy-fashion.

THE GREAT JOYS.—As stated in the text, shimmering dresses in soft and subtle shades : rose-awakening, water's-smile, amber-dew, blue-of-dawn, etc.

MATERNAL LOVE.—A costume very similar to the dress

worn by LIGHT, that is to say, supple and almost transparent veils, as of a Greek statue, and, in so far as possible, white. Pearls and other stones, as rich and numerous as may be desired, provided that they do not break the pure and candid harmony of the whole.

TIME.—Traditional dress of Time : a wide black or dark-blue cloak, a streaming white beard, scythe and hour-glass.

THE NEIGHBOUR'S LITTLE GIRL.—Bright fair hair ; a long white frock.

Other dresses as described in the text.

SCENES

THE BLUE BIRD

ACT I

The Wood-cutter's Cottage

The stage represents the interior of a wood-cutter's cottage, simple and rustic in appearance, but in no way poverty-stricken. A recessed fireplace containing the dying embers of a wood-fire. Kitchen utensils, a cupboard, a bread-pan, a grandfather's clock, a spinning-wheel, a water-tap, etc. On a table, a lighted lamp. At the foot of the cupboard, on either side, a DOG and a CAT lie sleeping, rolled up, each with its nose in its tail. Between them stands a large blue-and-white sugar-loaf. On the wall hangs a round cage containing a turtle-dove. At the back, two windows, with closed inside shutters. Under one of the windows, a stool. On the left is the front door, with a big latch to it. On the right another door. A ladder leads up to a loft. On the right also are two little children's cots, at the head of which are two chairs, with clothes carefully folded on them. When the curtain rises, TYLTYL and MYTYL are sound asleep in their cots. MUMMY TYL tucks them in, leans over them, watches them for a moment as they sleep and beckons to DADDY TYL, who thrusts his head through the half-open door. MUMMY TYL lays a finger on her lips, to impose silence upon him, and then goes out to the right, on tip-toe, after first putting out the lamp. The scene remains in darkness for a moment. Then a light, gradually increasing in intensity, filters in through the shutters. The lamp on the table lights again of itself. The two CHILDREN *appear to wake and sit up in bed.*

TYLTYL.   Mytyl?

MYTYL.   Tyltyl?

TYLTYL.   Are you asleep?

MYTYL.   Are you?

TYLTYL.   No; how can I be asleep when I am talking to you?

MYTYL.   I say, is this Christmas Day?

TYLTYL.   Not yet; not till to-morrow. But Father Christmas won't bring us anything this year.

MYTYL.   Why not?

TYLTYL.   I heard Mummy say that she couldn't go to town to tell him. But he will come next year.

MYTYL.   Is next year far off?

TYLTYL.   A good long while. But he will come to the rich children to-night.

MYTYL.   Really?

TYLTYL.   Hullo! Mummy's forgotten to put out the lamp! I've an idea!

MYTYL.   What?

TYLTYL.   Let's get up.

MYTYL.   But we mustn't.

TYLTYL.   Why, there's no one about. Do you see the shutters?

MYTYL.   Oh, how bright they are!

TYLTYL.   It's the lights of the party.

MYTYL.   What party?

TYLTYL.   The rich children opposite. It's the Christmas-tree. Let's open the shutters.

MYTYL.   Can we?

TYLTYL.   Of course; there's no one to stop us. Do you hear the music? Let us get up.

(*The two* CHILDREN *get up, run to one of the windows, climb on to the stool and throw back the shutters.*

MUMMY TYL WATCHES THE CHILDREN AS THEY SLEEP

A bright light fills the room.   The Children *look out greedily.)*

Tyltyl.   We can see everything !

Mytyl (*who can hardly find room on the stool*).   I can't.

Tyltyl.   It's snowing !   There are two carriages, with six horses each !

Mytyl.   There are twelve little boys getting out !

Tyltyl.   How silly you are !   They're little girls.

Mytyl.   They've got knickerbockers.

Tyltyl.   What do you know ?   Don't push so !

Mytyl.   I never touched you.

Tyltyl (*who is taking up the whole stool*).   You're taking all the room.

Mytyl.   Why, I have no room at all !

Tyltyl.   Do be quiet !   I see the tree !

Mytyl.   What tree ?

Tyltyl.   Why, the Christmas-tree !   You're looking at the wall !

Mytyl.   I'm looking at the wall because I have no room.

Tyltyl (*giving her a miserly little place on the stool*). There !   Will that do ?   Now you're better off than I ! I say, what lots and lots of lights !

Mytyl.   What are those people doing who are making such a noise ?

Tyltyl.   They're the musicians.

Mytyl.   Are they angry ?

Tyltyl.   No ; but it's hard work.

Mytyl.   Another carriage with white horses !

Tyltyl.   Be quiet !   And look !

Mytyl.   What are those gold things there, hanging from the branches ?

Tyltyl.   Why, toys, of course !   Swords, guns, soldiers, cannons.

Mytyl.   And dolls : I say, are there any dolls ?

TYLTYL. Dolls ? That's too silly ; there's no fun in dolls.

MYTYL. And what's that all round the table ?

TYLTYL. Cakes and fruit and tarts.

MYTYL. I had some once when I was little.

TYLTYL. So had I ; it's nicer than bread, but they don't give you enough.

MYTYL. They have plenty over there. The whole table's full. Are they going to eat them ?

TYLTYL. Certainly. What else would they do with them ?

MYTYL. Why don't they eat them at once ?

TYLTYL. Because they're not hungry.

MYTYL (*stupefied with astonishment*). Not hungry ? Why not ?

TYLTYL. Well, they eat whenever they want to.

MYTYL (*incredulously*). Every day ?

TYLTYL. So I'm told.

MYTYL. Will they eat them all ? Will they give any away ?

TYLTYL. To whom ?

MYTYL. To us.

TYLTYL. They don't know us.

MYTYL. Suppose we asked them.

TYLTYL. We mustn't.

MYTYL. Why not ?

TYLTYL. Because it's not right.

MYTYL (*clapping her hands*). Oh, how pretty they are !

TYLTYL (*rapturously*). And how they're laughing and laughing !

MYTYL. And the little ones dancing !

TYLTYL. Yes, yes ; let's dance too ! (*They stamp their feet for joy on the stool.*)

MYTYL. Oh, what fun !

TYLTYL. They're getting the cakes ! They can touch them ! They're eating, they're eating, they're eating !

MYTYL.   The tiny ones, too !   They've got two, three, four apiece !

TYLTYL (*drunk with delight*).   Oh, how lovely !   Oh, how lovely, how lovely !

MYTYL (*counting imaginary cakes*).   I've got a dozen !

TYLTYL.   And I four dozen !   But I'll give you some.

(*A knock at the door of the cottage.*)

TYLTYL (*suddenly quieted and frightened*).   What's that ?

MYTYL (*scared*).   It's Daddy !

(*As they hesitate before opening the door, the big latch is seen to rise of itself, with a grating sound ; the door half-opens to admit a little old woman dressed in green, with a red hood on her head. She is humpbacked and lame and near-sighted ; her nose and chin meet ; and she walks bent on a stick. She is obviously a fairy.*)

THE FAIRY.   Have you the grass here that sings or the bird that is blue ?

TYLTYL.   We have some grass, but it can't sing.

MYTYL.   Tyltyl has a bird.

TYLTYL.   But I can't give it away.

THE FAIRY.   Why not ?

TYLTYL.   Because it's mine.

THE FAIRY.   That's a reason, certainly.   Where is the bird ?

TYLTYL (*pointing to the cage*).   In the cage.

THE FAIRY (*putting on her glasses to examine the bird*). I don't want it ; it's not blue enough.   You will have to go and find me the one I want.

TYLTYL.   But I don't know where it is.

THE FAIRY.   No more do I.   That's why you must look for it.   I can do without the grass that sings, at a pinch ;

3

but I must absolutely have the Blue Bird. It's for my little girl, who is very ill.

TYLTYL. What's the matter with her?

THE FAIRY. We don't quite know; she wants to be happy.

TYLTYL. Really?

THE FAIRY. Do you know who I am?

TYLTYL. You're rather like our neighbour, Madame Berlingot.

THE FAIRY (*growing suddenly angry*). Not a bit! There's not the least likeness! This is intolerable! I am the Fairy Bérylune.

TYLTYL. Oh, very well!

THE FAIRY. You will have to start at once.

TYLTYL. Are you coming with us?

THE FAIRY. I can't, because I put on the soup this morning and it always boils over if I leave it for more than an hour. (*Pointing successively to the ceiling, the chimney and the window*) Will you go out this way, or that way, or that way?

TYLTYL (*pointing timidly to the door*). I would rather go out that way.

THE FAIRY (*growing suddenly angry again*). That's quite impossible; and it's a shocking habit! (*Pointing to the window*) We'll go out this way. Well? What are you waiting for? Get dressed at once. (*The* CHILDREN *do as they are told and dress quickly.*) I'll help Mytyl.

TYLTYL. We have no shoes.

THE FAIRY. That doesn't matter. I'm going to give you a little magic hat. Where are your father and mother?

TYLTYL (*pointing to the door on the right*). They're asleep in there.

THE FAIRY. And your grandpapa and grandmamma?

TYLTYL. They are dead.

THE FAIRY. And your little brothers and sisters. Have you any?

TYLTYL. Oh, yes ; three little brothers.

MYTYL. And four little sisters.

THE FAIRY. Where are they ?

TYLTYL. They are dead too.

THE FAIRY. Would you like to see them again ?

TYLTYL. Oh, yes ! At once ! Show them to us !

THE FAIRY. I haven't got them in my pocket. But this is very lucky ; you will see them when you go through the Land of Memory. It's on the way to the Blue Bird, just on the left, past the third turning. What were you doing when I knocked ?

TYLTYL. We were playing at eating cakes.

THE FAIRY. Have you any cakes ? Where are they ?

TYLTYL. In the house of the rich children. Come and look ; it's so lovely ! (*He drags the* FAIRY *to the window.*)

THE FAIRY (*at the window*). But it's the others who are eating them !

TYLTYL. Yes ; but we can see them eat.

THE FAIRY. Aren't you cross with them ?

TYLTYL. What for ?

THE FAIRY. For eating all the cakes. I think it's very wrong of them not to give you some.

TYLTYL. Not at all ; they're rich. I say, isn't it beautiful over there ?

THE FAIRY. It's no more beautiful there than here.

TYLTYL. Ugh ! It's darker here and smaller and there are no cakes.

THE FAIRY. It's exactly the same, only you can't see.

TYLTYL. Yes, I can ; and I have very good eyes. I can see the time on the church clock and Daddy can't.

THE FAIRY (*suddenly angry*). I tell you that you can't see ! How do you see me ? What do I look like ? (*An awkward silence from* TYLTYL.) Well, answer me, will you ? I want to know if you can see ! Am I pretty or ugly ? (*The silence grows more and more uncomfortable.*) Won't you answer ? Am I young or old ? Are my cheeks pink or yellow ? Perhaps you'll say I have a hump ?

TYLTYL (*in a conciliatory tone*). No, no ; it's not a big one.

THE FAIRY. Oh, yes, to look at you, anyone would think it enormous. Have I a hook nose and have I lost one of my eyes ?

TYLTYL. Oh, no, I don't say that. Who put it out ?

THE FAIRY (*growing more and more irritated*). But it's not out ! You wretched, impudent boy ! It's much finer than the other ; it's bigger and brighter and blue as the sky. And my hair, do you see that ? It's fair as the corn in the fields, it's like virgin gold ! And I've such heaps and heaps of it that it weighs my head down. It escapes on every side. Do you see it on my hands ? (*She holds out two lean wisps of grey hair.*)

TYLTYL. Yes, I see a little.

THE FAIRY (*indignantly*). A little ! Sheaves ! Armfuls ! Clusters ! Waves of gold ! I know there are people who say that they don't see any ; but you're not one of those wicked, blind people, I should hope ?

TYLTYL. Oh, no, I can see all that isn't hidden.

THE FAIRY. But you ought to see the rest with as little doubt ! Human beings are very odd ! Since the death of the fairies, they see nothing at all and they never suspect it. Luckily, I always carry with me all that is wanted to give new light to dimmed eyes. What am I taking out of my bag ?

TYLTYL. Oh, what a dear little green hat ! What's that shining in the cockade ?

THE FAIRY. That's the big diamond that makes people see.

TYLTYL. Really ?

THE FAIRY. Yes ; when you've got the hat on your head, you turn the diamond a little : from right to left, for instance, like this ; do you see ? Then it presses a bump which nobody knows of and which opens your eyes.

TYLTYL. Doesn't it hurt ?

THE FAIRY. On the contrary, it's enchanted. You
at once see even the inside of things : the soul of bread,
of wine, of pepper, for instance.

MYTYL. Can you see the soul of sugar, too ?

THE FAIRY (*suddenly cross*). Of course you can ! I
hate unnecessary questions. The soul of sugar is no more
interesting than the soul of pepper. There, I give you all
I have to help you in your search for the Blue Bird. I
know that the flying carpet or the ring which makes its
wearer invisible would be more useful to you. But I
have lost the key of the cupboard in which I locked them.
Oh, I was forgetting ! (*Pointing to the diamond.*) When
you hold it like this—do you see ?—one little turn more and
you behold the past. Another little turn and you behold
the future. It's curious and practical and it's quite
noiseless.

TYLTYL. Daddy will take if from me.

THE FAIRY. He won't see it ; no one can see it as
long as it's on your head. Will you try it ? (*She puts
the little green hat on* TYLTYL's *head.*) Now, turn the
diamond. One turn and then. . . . .

> (TYLTYL *has no sooner turned the diamond than a
> sudden and wonderful change comes over everything.
> The old* FAIRY *alters then and there into a princess
> of marvellous beauty ; the flints of which the cottage
> walls are built light up, turn blue as sapphires,
> become transparent and gleam and sparkle like the
> most precious stones. The humble furniture takes
> life and becomes resplendent ; the deal table assumes
> as grave and noble an air as a table made of
> marble ; the face of the clock winks its eye and
> smiles genially, while the door that contains the
> pendulum opens and releases the* HOURS, *who,
> holding one another by the hand and laughing
> merrily, begin to dance to the sound of delicious
> music.*)

TYLTYL (*displaying a legitimate bewilderment and point-ing to the* HOURS). Who are all those pretty ladies ?

THE FAIRY. Don't be afraid ; they are the hours of your life and they are glad to be free and visible for a moment.

TYLTYL. And why are the walls so bright ? Are they made of sugar or of precious stones ?

THE FAIRY. All stones are alike, all stones are precious ; but man sees only a few of them.

> (*While they are speaking, the scene of enchantment continues and is completed. The souls of the* QUARTERN-LOAVES, *in the form of little men in crust-coloured tights, flurried and powdered with flour, scramble out of the bread pan and frisk round the table, where they are joined by* FIRE, *who, springing from the hearth in yellow and vermilion tights, writhes with laughter as he chases the loaves.*)

TYLTYL. Who are those ugly little men ?

THE FAIRY. Oh, they're nothing much ; they are the souls of the Quartern-loaves, who are taking advantage of the reign of truth to leave the pan in which they were too tightly packed.

TYLTYL. And the big red fellow, with the nasty smell ?

THE FAIRY. Hush ! Don't speak too loud ; that's Fire. He's dangerous.

> (*This dialogue does not interrupt the enchantment. The* DOG *and the* CAT, *lying rolled up at the foot of the cupboard, utter a loud and simultaneous cry and disappear down a trap ; and in their places rise two persons, one of whom has the face of a bull-dog, the other that of a tom-cat. Forthwith, the little man with the bull-dog face, whom we will hencefor-ward call the* DOG, *rushes upon* TYLTYL, *kisses him*

violently and overwhelms him with noisy and im-
petuous caresses; while the little woman with the
face of a cat, whom we will simply call the CAT,
combs her hair, washes her hands and strokes her
whiskers before going up to MYTYL.)

THE DOG (*yelling, jumping about, knocking up against
everything, generally unbearable*). My little god! Good-
morning, good-morning, my little god! At last, at last
we can talk! I had so much to tell you! Bark and wag
my tail as I might, you never understood! But now!
Good-morning, good-morning! I love you! I love
you! Shall I do some of my tricks? Shall I beg?
Would you like to see me walk on my front-paws or dance
on my hind-legs?

TYLTYL (*to the* FAIRY). Who is this gentleman with
the dog's head?

THE FAIRY. Don't you see? It's the soul of TYLÔ,
whom you have set free.

THE CAT (*going up to* MYTYL *and putting out her hand to
her, with much ceremony and circumspection*). Good-
morning, miss. How well you look this morning!

MYTYL. Good-morning, ma'am. (*To the* FAIRY) Who
is it?

THE FAIRY. Why, don't you see? It's the soul of
Tylette offering you her hand. Kiss her.

THE DOG (*hustling the* CAT). Me too! I've kissed the
little god! I've kissed the little girl! I've kissed everybody! Oh, grand! What fun we shall have! I'm
going to frighten Tylette! Bow, bow, wow!

THE CAT. Sir, I don't know you.

THE FAIRY (*threatening the* DOG *with her stick*). Keep
still, will you, or else you'll go back into silence until the
end of time.

(*Meanwhile the enchantment has pursued its course:
the spinning-wheel has begun to turn madly in its*

corner and to spin brilliant rays of light ; the tap,
in another corner, begins to sing in a very high
voice, and turning into a luminous fountain, floods
the sink with sheets of pearls and emeralds, through
which darts the soul of WATER, *like a young girl,*
streaming, dishevelled and tearful, who immediately
begins to fight with FIRE.)

TYLTYL. And who is that wet lady ?
THE FAIRY. Don't be afraid, it's Water just come from
the tap.

(The milk-jug upsets, falls from the table and smashes
on the floor ; and from the spilt milk there rises
a tall, white, bashful figure who seems to be afraid
of everything.)

TYLTYL. And the frightened lady in her nightgown ?
THE FAIRY. That's Milk ; she has broken her jug.

(The sugar-loaf, at the foot of the cupboard, grows taller
and wider and splits its paper wrapper, whence
issues a mawkish and hypocritical creature, dressed
in a long coat half blue and half white, who goes
up to MYTYL *with a sanctimonious smile.)*

MYTYL (*greatly alarmed*). What does he want ?
THE FAIRY. Why, he is the soul of Sugar !
MYTYL (*reassured*). Has he any barley-sugar ?
THE FAIRY. His pockets are full of it and each of his
fingers is a sugar-stick.

(The lamp falls from the table and, at the same moment,
its flame springs up again and turns into a
luminous maid of incomparable beauty. She is
dressed in long, transparent and dazzling veils and
stands motionless in a sort of ecstasy.)

TYLTYL.　It's the Queen !
MYTYL.　It's the Blessed Virgin !
THE FAIRY.　No, my children ; it's Light.

(Meanwhile, the saucepans on the shelves spin round like tops ; the linen-press throws open its folding-doors and unrolls a magnificent display of moon-coloured and sun-coloured stuffs, with which mingles a no less splendid array of rags and tatters that come down the ladder from the loft. But, suddenly, three loud knocks are heard on the door at the right.)

TYLTYL (*alarmed*).　That's Daddy !　He's heard us !
THE FAIRY.　Turn the diamond !　From left to right !　(TYLTYL *turns the diamond quickly.*)　Not so quick !　Heavens !　It's too late !　You turned it too briskly ; they will not have time to resume their places and we shall have a lot of trouble.

(The FAIRY becomes an old woman again ; the walls of the cottage lose their splendour. The HOURS go back into the clock, the spinning-wheel stops, etc. But, in the general hurry and confusion, while FIRE runs madly round the room, looking for the chimney, one of the QUARTERN-LOAVES OF BREAD, who has been unable to squeeze into the pan, bursts into sobs and utters roars of fright.)

THE FAIRY.　What's the matter ?
BREAD (*in tears*).　There's no room in the pan !
THE FAIRY (*stooping over the pan*).　Yes, there is ; yes, there is.　(*Pushing the other* LOAVES, *who have resumed their original places*)　Come, quick, make room there.

(The knocking at the door is renewed.)

4

ACT II

Scene I. *At the Fairy's*

A magnificent entrance-hall in the palace of the FAIRY
BÉRYLUNE. *Columns of gleaming marble with gold
and silver capitals, staircases, porticoes, balustrades, etc.*

Enter from the back, on the right, sumptuously clad, the CAT,
SUGAR *and* FIRE. *They come from a room which emits
rays of light ; it is the* FAIRY'S *wardrobe. The* CAT
has donned a light gauze veil over her black silk tights ;
SUGAR *has a silk dress, half white and half pale-blue ;
and* FIRE *wears a number of many-coloured aigrettes
and a long crimson mantle lined with gold. They cross
the whole length of the hall to the front of the stage, where
the* CAT *draws them up under a portico on the right.*

THE CAT. This way. I know every inch of this palace.
It was left to the Fairy Bérylune by Bluebeard. Let us
make the most of our last minute of liberty, while the
Children and Light pay their visit to the Fairy's little
daughter. I have brought you here to discuss the position
in which we are placed. Are we all present ?

SUGAR. I see the Dog coming out of the Fairy's wardrobe.

FIRE. What on earth is he wearing ?

THE CAT. He has put on the livery of one of the foot-
men of Cinderella's coach. It's the very thing for him.
He has the soul of a flunkey. But let us hide behind the
balustrade. It's strange how I mistrust him. He had
better not hear what I have to say to you.

SUGAR. It is too late. He has scented us. Look,

24

here is Water coming out of the wardrobe also.   Goodness me, how fine she is !

(The Dog *and* Water *join the first group.)*

The Dog *(frisking about).*   There !   There !   Aren't we fine !   Just look at these laces and this embroidery !   It's real gold and no mistake !

The Cat *(to* Water*).*   Is that Catskin's "colour-of-time " dress ?   I seem to know it.

Water.   Yes, it's the one that suited me best.

Fire *(between his teeth).*   She's not brought her umbrella.

Water.   What's that ?

Fire.   Nothing, nothing.

Water.   I thought you might be speaking of a great red nose I saw the other day.

The Cat.   Come, don't let us quarrel ; we have more important things to do.   We are only waiting for Bread : where is he ?

The Dog.   He was making an endless fuss about choosing his dress.

Fire.   Worth while, isn't it, for a fellow who looks like an idiot and carries an enormous stomach ?

The Dog.   At last, he decided in favour of a Turkish robe, adorned with gems, a scimitar and a turban.

The Cat.   There he is !   He has put on Bluebeard's finest dress.

> *Enter* Bread, *in the costume described above.   The silk robe is crossed tightly over his huge stomach.   In one hand he holds the hilt of a scimitar passed through his sash and, in the other, the cage intended for the Blue Bird.*

Bread *(waddling conceitedly).*   Well ?   What do you think of this ?

The Dog *(frisking round* Bread*).*   How nice he looks !

What a fool he looks !   How nice he looks !   How nice he looks !

THE CAT (*to* BREAD).   Are the children dressed ?

BREAD.   Yes, Master Tyltyl has put on Hop-o'-my-Thumb's blue jacket, white stockings and red breeches ; and Miss Mytyl has Gretel's frock and Cinderella's slippers. But the great thing was the dressing of Light !

THE CAT.   Why ?

BREAD.   The Fairy thought her so lovely that she did not want to dress her at all !   Thereupon I protested in the name of our dignity as essential and eminently respectable elements ; and I ended by declaring that, under those conditions, I should refuse to be seen with her.

FIRE.   They ought to have bought her a lamp-shade !

THE CAT.   And what answer did the Fairy make ?

BREAD.   She hit me with her stick on my head and stomach.

THE CAT.   And then ?

BREAD.   I was promptly convinced ; but, at the last moment, Light decided on the moonbeam dress at the bottom of the chest with Catskin's treasures.

THE CAT.   Come, stop chattering, time presses.   Our future is at stake.   You have heard—the Fairy has just said so—that the end of this journey will, at the same time, mark the end of our lives.   It is our business, therefore, to prolong it as much as possible and by every possible means.   But there is another thing : we must think of the fate of our race and the destiny of our children.

BREAD.   Hear, hear !   The Cat is right !

THE CAT.   Listen to me !   All of us here present, Animals, Things and Elements, possess a soul which man does not yet know.   That is why we retain a remnant of independence ; but, if he finds the Blue Bird, he will know all, he will see all and we shall be completely at his mercy.   This is what I have just learned from my old friend Night, who is also the guardian of the mysteries of Life.   It is to our interest, therefore, at all costs to prevent the finding of that bird, even if we have to go so far as to endanger the lives of the children themselves.

THE DOG (*indignantly*). What's the hussy saying? Just say that again, will you, to see if I heard right?

BREAD. Order! Order! It's not your turn to speak! I'm in the chair at this meeting.

FIRE. Who made you chairman?

WATER (*to* FIRE). Hold your tongue! What are you interfering for?

FIRE. I shall interfere if I choose. And I want none of your remarks.

SUGAR (*conciliatorily*). Excuse me. Do not let us quarrel. This is a serious moment. We must, above all things, decide what measures to adopt.

BREAD. I quite agree with Sugar and the Cat.

THE DOG. This is ridiculous! There is Man and that's all! We have to obey him and do as he tells us! That is the one and only fact! I recognize no one but him! Hurrah for Man! Man for ever! In life or death, all for Man! Man is God!

BREAD. I quite agree with the Dog.

THE CAT (*to the* DOG). But at least give your reasons.

THE DOG. There are no reasons! I love Man and that's enough! If you do anything against him, I will throttle you first and I will go and tell him everything.

SUGAR (*intervening sweetly*). Excuse me. Let us not embitter the discussion. From a certain point of view, you are both of you right. There is something to be said on both sides.

BREAD. I quite agree with Sugar.

THE CAT. Are we not, all of us, Water, Fire and you yourselves, Bread and the Dog, the victims of a nameless tyranny! Do you remember the time when, before the coming of the despot, we wandered freely over the face of the earth? Fire and Water were the sole masters of the world; and see what they have come to! As for us puny descendants of the great wild animals. . . . . Look out ! Pretend to be doing nothing ! I see the Fairy and Light coming. Light has taken sides with Man ; she is our worst enemy. Here they are.

Enter, on the right, the FAIRY *and* LIGHT, *followed by* TYLTYL *and* MYTYL.

THE FAIRY. Well ? What is it ? What are you doing in that corner ? You look like conspirators. It is time to start. I have decided that Light shall be your leader. You will obey her as you would me and I am giving her my wand. The children will pay a visit to their late grandparents this evening. You will remain behind ; that is more discreet. They will spend the evening in the bosom of their dead family. Meanwhile you will be getting ready all that is wanted for to-morrow's journey, which will be a long one. Come, up, be off and every one to his post !

THE CAT (*hypocritically*). That is just what I was saying to them, madam. I was encouraging them to do their whole duty bravely and conscientiously ; unfortunately, the Dog, who kept on interrupting me . . .

THE DOG. What's that ? Just wait a bit !

(*He is about to leap upon the* CAT, *but* TYLTYL, *foreseeing his intention, stops him with a threatening gesture.*)

TYLTYL. Down, Tylô ! Take care ; and, if ever I catch you again . . .

THE DOG. My little god, you don't know, it was she who . . .

TYLTYL (*threatening him*). Be quiet !

THE FAIRY. Come, that will do. Let Bread hand the cage for this evening to Tyltyl. It is just possible that the Blue Bird may be hidden in the Past, at the grandparents'. In any case, it is a chance which we must not neglect. Well, Bread, the cage ?

BREAD (*solemnly*). One moment, if you please, Mrs. Fairy. (*Like an orator making a speech*) I call upon all of you to bear witness that this silver cage, which was entrusted to my care by . . .

THE FAIRY (*interrupting him*). Enough ! No speeches ! We will go out this way and the children that.

TYLTYL (*rather anxiously*). Are we to go all alone ?

MYTYL. I am hungry !

TYLTYL. I too !

THE FAIRY (*to* BREAD). Open your Turkish robe and give them a slice of your good stomach.

> (*Bread opens his robe, draws his scimitar, cuts two slices out of his stomach and hands them to the* CHILDREN.)

SUGAR (*approaching the* CHILDREN). Allow me at the same time to offer you a few sugar-sticks.

> (*He breaks off the five fingers of his left hand, one by one, and presents them to the* CHILDREN.)

MYTYL. What is he doing ? He is breaking all his fingers !

SUGAR (*engagingly*). Taste them, they are capital. They're made of real barley-sugar.

MYTYL (*sucking one of the fingers*). Oh, how good they are ! Have you many of them ?

SUGAR (*modestly*). Yes ; as many as I want.

MYTYL. Does that hurt you much, when you break them off ?

SUGAR. Not at all. On the contrary, it's a great advantage : they grow again at once and so I always have new, clean fingers.

THE FAIRY. Come, children, don't eat too much

5

sugar.   Don't forget that you are to have supper presently
with your grandpapa and grandmamma.

TYLTYL.   Are they here ?

THE FAIRY.   You shall see them at once.

TYLTYL.   How can we see them, when they are dead ?

THE FAIRY.   How can they be dead, when they live
in your memory ?   Men do not know this secret, because
they know so little ; whereas you, thanks to the diamond,
are about to see that the Dead who are remembered live
as happily as though they were not dead.

TYLTYL.   Is Light coming with us ?

THE FAIRY.   No, it is more proper that this visit should
be confined to the family.   I will wait near here, so as not
to appear indiscreet.   They did not invite me.

TYLTYL.   Which way are we to go ?

THE FAIRY.   Over there.   You are on the threshold
of the Land of Memory.   As soon as you have turned the
diamond, you will see a big tree with a board on it, which
will show you that you are there.   But don't forget that
you are to be back, both of you, by a quarter to nine.   It
is most important.   Now mind and be punctual, for all
would be lost if you were late.   Good-bye for the present !
(*Calling the* CAT, *the* DOG, LIGHT, *etc.*) This way.   And
the little ones that way.

(*She goes out to the right, with* LIGHT, *the* ANIMALS, *etc.,*
while the CHILDREN *go out to the left.*)

CURTAIN

SCENE II.   *The Land of Memory*

A thick fog, from which stands out, on the right, close to the
footlights, the trunk of a large oak, with a board nailed

THE LAND OF MEMORY

to it. A milky, diffused, impenetrable light prevails.
TYLTYL *and* MYTYL *are at the foot of the oak.*

TYLTYL.   Here is the tree !

MYTYL.   There's the board !

TYLTYL.   I can't read it.   Wait, I will climb up on this root.   That's it.   It says, " Land of Memory."

MYTYL.   Is this where it begins ?

TYLTYL.   Yes, there's an arrow.

MYTYL.   Well, where are Grandad and Granny ?

TYLTYL.   Behind the fog.   We shall see.

MYTYL.   I can see nothing at all !   I can't see my feet or my hands.   (*Whimpering*) I'm cold !   I don't want to travel any more.   I want to go home.

TYLTYL.   Come, don't keep on crying, just like Water. You ought to be ashamed of yourself.   A great big little girl like you !   Look, the fog is lifting already.   We shall see what's behind it.

(*The mist begins to move ; it grows thinner and lighter, disperses, evaporates.   Soon, in a more and more transparent light, appears, under a leafy vault, a cheerful little peasant's cottage, covered with creepers. The door and windows are open.   There are bee-hives under a shed, flower-pots on the window-sills, a cage with a sleeping blackbird.   Beside the door is a bench, on which an old peasant and his wife,* TYLTYL's *grandfather and grandmother, are seated, both sound asleep.*)

TYLTYL (*suddenly recognizing them*).   It's Grandad and Granny !

MYTYL (*clapping her hands*).   Yes ! Yes ! So it is ! So it is !

TYLTYL (*still a little distrustful*).   Take care.   We don't know yet if they can stir.   Let's keep behind the tree.

(GRANNY TYL *opens her eyes, raises her head, stretches herself, gives a sigh and looks at* GAFFER TYL, *who also wakes slowly from his sleep.*)

GRANNY TYL.   I have a notion that our grandchildren who are still alive are coming to see us to-day.

GAFFER TYL.   They are certainly thinking of us, for I feel anyhow and I have pins and needles in my legs.

GRANNY TYL.   I think they must be quite near, for I see tears of joy dancing before my eyes.

GAFFER TYL.   No, no, they are a long way off.   I still feel weak.

GRANNY TYL.   I tell you they are here; I am quite strong.

TYLTYL *and* MYTYL (*rushing up from behind the oak*). Here we are !   Here we are !   Grandad !   Granny !   It's we !   It's we !

GAFFER TYL.   There !   You see ?   What did I tell you ?   I was sure they would come to-day.

GRANNY TYL.   Tyltyl !   Mytyl !   It's you !   It's she ! It's both of them !   (*Trying to run to meet them*) I can't run !   I've still got the rheumatics !

GAFFER TYL (*hobbling along as fast as he can*).   No more can I.   That's because of my wooden leg, which I still wear instead of the one I broke when I fell off the big oak.

(The GRANDPARENTS *and the* CHILDREN *exchange frantic embraces.*)

GRANNY TYL.   How tall and strong you've grown, Tyltyl !

GAFFER TYL (*stroking* MYTYL'S *hair*).   And Mytyl ! Just look at her.   What pretty hair, what pretty eyes ! And how sweet she smells !

GRANNY TYL.   Come and kiss me again !   Come on to my lap.

GAFFER TYL. And what about me ?

GRANNY TYL. No, no. Come to me first. How are Daddy and Mummy Tyl ?

TYLTYL. Quite well, Granny. They were asleep when we went out.

GRANNY TYL (*gazing at them and covering them with caresses*). Lord, how pretty they are and how nice and clean ! Did Mummy wash you ? And there are no holes in your stockings ! I used to darn them once, you know. Why don't you come to see us oftener ? It makes us so happy ! It is months and months that you've forgotten us and that we have seen nobody.

TYLTYL. We couldn't, Granny ; and to-day it's only because of the Fairy.

GRANNY TYL. We are always here, waiting for a visit from those who are alive. They come so seldom ! The last time you were here, let me see, when was it ? It was on All-hallows, when the church-bells were ringing.

TYLTYL. All-hallows ? We didn't go out that day, for we both had bad colds.

GRANNY TYL. No ; but you thought of us.

TYLTYL. Yes.

GRANNY TYL. Well, every time you think of us, we wake up and see you again.

TYLTYL. What, is it enough to . . . ?

GRANNY TYL. But come, you know that.

TYLTYL. No, I didn't know.

GRANNY TYL (*to* GAFFER TYL). It's astonishing, up there. They don't know yet. Do they never learn anything ?

GAFFER TYL. It's as in our own time. The Living are so stupid when they speak of the Others.

TYLTYL. Do you sleep all the time ?

GAFFER TYL. Yes, we get plenty of sleep, while waiting for a thought of the Living to come and wake us. Ah, it is good to sleep, when life is done ! But it is pleasant also to wake up from time to time.

TYLTYL.   So you are not really dead ?

GAFFER TYL (*giving a start*).   What do you say ?   What is he talking about ?   Now he's using words which we don't understand.   Is it a new word, a new invention ?

TYLTYL.   The word " dead " ?

GAFFER TYL.   Yes, that was the word.   What does it mean ?

TYLTYL.   Why, it means that one's no longer alive.

GAFFER TYL.   How silly they are, up there !

TYLTYL.   Is it nice here ?

GAFFER TYL.   Oh, yes ; not bad, not bad ; and, if people still prayed for us . .

TYLTYL.   Daddy told me to stop praying.

GAFFER TYL.   Nonsense, nonsense.   Praying means remembering.

GRANNY TYL.   Yes, yes, all would be well, if only you would come and see us oftener.   Do you remember, Tyltyl ?   Last time, I made you a lovely apple-tart. You ate such a lot of it that you made yourself ill.

TYLTYL.   But I haven't eaten any apple-tart since last year.   There were no apples this year.

GRANNY TYL.   Don't be silly.   We always have them here.

TYLTYL.   That's different.

GRANNY TYL.   What ?   That's different ?   Why, nothing's different when we're able to kiss each other.

TYLTYL (*looking first at his* GRANDMOTHER *and then at his* GRANDFATHER).   You haven't changed, Grandad, not a bit, not a bit.   And Granny hasn't changed a bit either.   But you're better-looking.

GAFFER TYL.   Well, we feel all right.   We have stopped growing older.   But you, how tall you're growing !   Yes, you're shooting up finely.   Look, over there, on the door, is the mark of last time.   That was on All-hallows.   Now then, stand up straight.   (TYLTYL *stands up against the door.*)   Four fingers !   That's immense !   (MYTYL *also stands against the door.*)   And Mytyl, four and a half !

Aha, ill weeds wax apace! How they've grown, how they've grown!

TYLTYL (*looking around him with delight*). Nothing is changed, everything is in its old place! Only everything is prettier! There is the clock with the big hand which I broke the point of.

GAFFER TYL. And here is the soup-tureen you chipped a corner off.

TYLTYL. And here is the hole which I made in the door, the day I found the gimlet.

GAFFER TYL. Yes, you've done some damage in your time! And here is the plum-tree in which you were so fond of climbing, when I wasn't looking. It still has those fine red plums.

TYLTYL. Why, they're finer than ever!

MYTYL. And here is the old blackbird! Does he still sing?

(*The blackbird wakes and begins to sing at the top of his voice.*)

GRANNY TYL. You see. As soon as one thinks of him.

TYLTYL (*observing with amazement that the blackbird is quite blue*). But he's blue! Why, that's the bird, the Blue Bird which I am to take back to the Fairy. And you never told us that you had him here! Oh, he's blue, blue, blue as a blue glass marble! (*Entreatingly*) Grandad, Granny, will you give him to me?

GAFFER TYL. Yes, perhaps, perhaps. What do you think, Granny Tyl?

GRANNY TYL. Certainly, certainly. What use is he to us? He does nothing but sleep. We never hear him sing.

TYLTYL. I will put him in my cage. I say, where is my cage? Oh, I know, I left it behind the big tree. (*He runs to the tree, fetches the cage and puts the blackbird into it.*) So really, you've really given him to me ? How pleased the Fairy will be ! And Light too !

GAFFER TYL. Mind you, I won't answer for the bird. I'm afraid that he will never get used again to the restless life up there and that he'll come back here by the first wind that blows. However, we shall see. Leave him there, for the present, and come and look at the cow.

TYLTYL (*noticing the hives*). And how are the bees getting on ?

GAFFER TYL. Oh, pretty well. They are no longer alive, as you call it up there ; but they work steadily.

TYLTYL (*going up to the hives*). Oh, yes ! I can smell the honey ! How heavy the hives must be ! All the flowers are so beautiful ! And my little dead sisters, are they here too ?

MYTYL. And where are my three little brothers who were buried ?

(*At these words, seven little* CHILDREN, *of different sizes, like a set of Pan's pipes, come out of the cottage, one by one.*)

GRANNY TYL. Here they are, here they are ! As soon as you think of them, as soon as you speak of them, they are there, the darlings !

(TYLTYL *and* MYTYL *run to meet the* CHILDREN. *They hustle and hug one another and dance and whirl about and utter screams of joy.*)

TYLTYL. Hullo, Pierrot ! (*They clutch each other by the hair.*) Ah, so we're going to fight again, as in the old days ! And Robert ! I say, Jean, what's become of your top ? Madeleine and Pierrette and Pauline ! And here's Riquette !

MYTYL. Oh, Riquette, Riquette ! She's still crawling on all fours !

Granny Tyl.   Yes, she has stopped growing.

Tyltyl (*noticing the little dog yelping around them*) There's Kiki, whose tail I cut off with Pauline's scissors. He hasn't changed either.

Gaffer Tyl (*sententiously*).   No, nothing changes here.

Tyltyl.   And Pauline still has a pimple on her nose !

Granny Tyl.   Yes, it won't go away ; there's nothing to be done for it.

Tyltyl.   Oh, how well they look, how fat and sleek they are !   What jolly cheeks they have !   They look well fed.

Granny Tyl.   They have been much better since they ceased living.   There's nothing more to fear, nobody is ever ill, one has no anxiety.

(*The clock inside the cottage strikes eight.*)

Granny Tyl (*amazed*).   What's that ?

Gaffer Tyl.   I don't know, I'm sure.   It must be the clock.

Granny Tyl.   It can't be.   It never strikes.

Gaffer Tyl.   Because we no longer think of the time. Was anyone thinking of the time ?

Tyltyl.   Yes, I was.   What is the time ?

Gaffer Tyl.   I'm sure I can't tell.   I've forgotten how. It struck eight times, so I suppose it's what they call eight o'clock up there.

Tyltyl.   Light expects me at a quarter to nine.   It's because of the Fairy.   It's most important.   I'm off !

Granny Tyl.   Don't leave us like that, just as supper's ready !   Quick, quick, let's lay the table outside.   I've got some capital cabbage-soup and a beautiful plum-tart.

(*They get out the table, dishes, plates, etc., and lay for supper outside the door, all helping.*)

Tyltyl.   Well, as I've got the Blue Bird. . . . And then

6

it's so long since I tasted cabbage-soup. . . . Ever since I've been travelling. They don't have it at the hotels.

Granny Tyl. There! That didn't take long! Sit down, children. Don't let us lose time, if you're in a hurry.

> (*They have lit the lamp and served the soup. The* Grandparents *and the* Children *sit down round the table jostling and elbowing one another and laughing and screaming with pleasure.*)

Tyltyl (*eating like a glutton*). How good it is ! Oh, how good it is ! I want some more ! More ! (*He brandishes his wooden spoon and noisily hits his plate with it.*)

Gaffer Tyl. Come, come, a little more quiet. You're just as ill-behaved as ever ; and you'll break your plate.

Tyltyl (*half-raising himself on his stool*). I want more, more ! (*He seizes the tureen, drags it toward him and upsets it and the soup, which trickles over the table and down upon their knees and scalds them. Yells, and screams of pain.*)

Granny Tyl. There ! I told you so !

Gaffer Tyl (*giving* Tyltyl *a loud box on the ear*). That's one for you !

Tyltyl (*staggered for a moment, next puts his hand to his cheek with an expression of rapture*). Oh, that's just like the slaps you used to give me when you were alive ! Grandad, how nice it was and how good it makes one feel ! I must give you a kiss !

Gaffer Tyl. Very well ; there's more where that came from, if you like them.

> (*The clock strikes half-past eight.*)

Tyltyl (*starting up*). Half-past eight ! (*He flings down his spoon.*) Mytyl, we've only just got time !

'GIVE ME YOUR HAND, LITTLE BROTHER. I FEEL SO FRIGHTENED AND SO COLD'

GRANNY TYL. Oh, I say! Just a few minutes more!
Your house isn't on fire! We see you so seldom.

TYLTYL. No, we can't possibly. Light is so kind.
And I promised her. Come, Mytyl, come!

GAFFER TYL. Goodness gracious, how tiresome the
living are with all their business and excitement!

TYLTYL (*taking his cage and hurriedly kissing everybody
all round*). Good-bye, Grandad. Good-bye, Granny.
Good-bye, brothers and sisters, Pierrot, Robert, Pauline,
Madeleine, Riquette; and you too, Kiki. I feel we
mustn't stay. Don't cry, Granny: we will come back
often.

GRANNY TYL. Come back every day!

TYLTYL. Yes, yes; we will come back as often as we
can.

GRANNY TYL. It's our only pleasure and it's such a
treat for us when your thoughts visit us!

GAFFER TYL. We have no other amusements.

TYLTYL. Quick, quick! My cage! My bird!

GAFFER TYL (*handing him the cage*). Here they are!
You know, I don't warrant him; and if he's not the right
colour . . .

TYLTYL. Good-bye! Good-bye!

THE BROTHERS AND SISTERS TYL. Good-bye, Tyltyl!
Good-bye, Mytyl! Remember the barley-sugar! Good-
bye! Come again! Come again!

(*They all wave their handkerchiefs while* TYLTYL *and*
MYTYL *slowly move away. But already, during
the last sentences, the fog of the beginning of the
scene has been gradually re-forming and the sound
of the voices dying away, so that, at the end, all has
disappeared in the mist and, at the fall of the
curtain,* TYLTYL *and* MYTYL *are again alone
visible under the big oak.*)

TYLTYL. It's this way, Mytyl.

MYTYL.   Where is Light ?

TYLTYL.   I don't know. (*Looking at the bird in the cage*) I say, the bird is no longer blue ! He has turned black !

MYTYL.   Give me your hand, little brother. I feel so frightened and so cold.

CURTAIN

SLEEP, NIGHT AND DEATH

ACT III

Scene I. *The Palace of Night*

A large and wonderful hall of an austere, rigid, metallic and sepulchral magnificence, giving the impression of a Greek or Egyptian temple, with columns, architraves, flagstones and ornaments of black marble, gold and ebony. The hall is trapezium-shaped. Basalt steps, occupying almost the entire width, divide it into three successive stages, which rise gradually toward the back. On the right and left, between the columns, are doors of sombre bronze. At the back, a monumental door of brass. The palace is lit only by a diffused light that seems to emanate mainly from the brilliancy of the marble and the ebony. At the rise of the curtain, NIGHT, in the shape of a very beautiful woman, clad in long, black garments, is seated on the steps of the second stage, between two children, of whom one, almost naked, like Cupid, is smiling in a deep sleep, while the other is standing up, motionless and veiled from head to foot.

Enter, from the right, in the foreground, the CAT.

NIGHT. Who goes there ?

THE CAT (*sinking heavily upon the marble steps*). It is I, Mother Night. I am worn out.

NIGHT. What's the matter, child ? You look pale and thin and you are splashed with mud to your very whiskers. Have you been fighting on the tiles again, in the snow and rain ?

THE CAT. It has nothing to do with the tiles ! It's

41

our secret that's at stake! It's the beginning of the end! I managed to escape for a moment, to warn you; but I fear that there is nothing to be done.

NIGHT. Why? What has happened?

THE CAT. I have told you of little Tyltyl, the wood-cutter's son, and of the magic diamond. Well, he is coming here to demand the Blue Bird of you.

NIGHT. He hasn't got him yet.

THE CAT. He will have him soon, unless we perform some miracle. This is how the matter stands: Light, who is guiding him and betraying us all, for she has placed herself entirely on Man's side, Light has learned that the Blue Bird, the real one, the only one that can live in the light of day, is hidden here, among the blue birds of the dreams that live on the moonbeams and die as soon as they set eyes on the sun. She knows that she is forbidden to cross the threshold of your palace, but she is sending the children; and, as you cannot prevent Man from opening the doors of your secrets, I do not know how all this will end. In any case, if, unfortunately, they should lay their hands on the real Blue Bird, there would be nothing for us but to disappear.

NIGHT. Oh dear, oh dear! What times we live in! I never have a moment's peace. I cannot understand Man, these last few years. What is he aiming at? Must he know everything? He has already captured a third of my Mysteries; all my Terrors are afraid and dare not leave the house; my Ghosts have taken flight; the greater part of my Sicknesses are ill.

THE CAT. I know, Mother Night, I know, the times are hard and we are almost alone in our struggle against Man. But I hear them coming. I see only one way: as they are children, we must give them such a fright that they will not dare to persist or to open the great door at the back, behind which they would find the birds of the Moon. The secrets of the other caverns will be enough to distract their attention and terrify them.

NIGHT (*listening to a sound outside*).   What do I hear ?
Are there many of them ?

THE CAT.   It is nothing ; it is our friends, Bread and
Sugar ; Water is not very well and Fire could not come,
because he is a kinsman of Light.   The Dog is the only one
who is not on our side ; but it is never possible to keep
him away.

Enter timidly, on the right, in the foreground, TYLTYL,
MYTYL, BREAD, SUGAR *and the* DOG.

THE CAT (*rushing up to* TYLTYL).   This way, little
master, this way.   I have told Night, who is delighted to
see you.   You must forgive her, she is a little indisposed ;
that is why she could not come to meet you.

TYLTYL.   Good-day, Mrs. Night.

NIGHT (*in an offended tone*).   Good-day ?   I am not
used to that.   You might say, Good-night, or, at least,
Good-evening.

TYLTYL (*mortified*).   I beg your pardon, ma'am.   I
did not know.   (*Pointing to the two* CHILDREN.)   Are those
your two little boys ?   They are very nice.

NIGHT.   Yes, this is Sleep.

TYLTYL.   Why is he so fat ?

NIGHT.   That is because he sleeps well.

TYLTYL.   And the other, hiding himself ?   Why does he
veil his face ?   Is he ill.   What is his name ?

NIGHT.   That is Sleep's sister.   It is better not to men-
tion her name.

TYLTYL.   Why ?

NIGHT.   Because her name is not pleasant to hear.   But
let us talk of something else.   The Cat tells me that you
have come here to look for the Blue Bird.

TYLTYL.   Yes, ma'am, if you will allow me.   Will you
tell me where he is ?

NIGHT.   I don't know, dear.   All I can say is that he is
not here.   I have never seen him.

TYLTYL. Yes, yes. Light told me that he was here; and Light knows what she is saying. Will you hand me your keys?

NIGHT. But you must understand, dear, that I cannot give my keys like that to the first comer. I have the keeping of all Nature's secrets, I am responsible for them and I am absolutely forbidden to deliver them to anybody, especially to a child.

TYLTYL. You have no right to refuse them to Man when he asks you for them. I know that.

NIGHT. Who told you?

TYLTYL. Light.

NIGHT. Light again! Always Light! How dare she interfere, how dare she?

THE DOG. Shall I take them from her by force, my little god?

TYLTYL. Hold your tongue, keep quiet and behave yourself. (*To* NIGHT) Come, madam, give me your keys, please.

NIGHT. Have you the sign, at least? Where is it?

TYLTYL (*touching his hat*). Behold the Diamond!

NIGHT (*resigning herself to the inevitable*). Well, then . . . Here is the key that opens all the doors of the hall. Look to yourself if you meet with a misfortune. I will not be answerable.

BREAD (*very anxiously*). Is it dangerous?

NIGHT. Dangerous? I will go so far as to say that I myself do not know what I shall do when certain of those bronze doors open upon the abyss. All around the hall, in each of those basalt caves, are all the Evils, all the Plagues, all the Sicknesses, all the Terrors, all the Catastrophes, all the Mysteries that have afflicted life since the beginning of the world. I have had trouble enough to imprison them there with the aid of Destiny; and it is not without difficulty, I assure you, that I keep some little order among those undisciplined characters. You have seen what happens when one of them slips out and shows itself on earth.

BREAD. My great age, my experience and my devotion make me the natural protector of these two children ; therefore, Mrs. Night, permit me to ask you a question.

NIGHT. Certainly.

BREAD. In case of danger, which is the way of escape ?

NIGHT. There is no way of escape.

TYLTYL (*taking the key and climbing the first steps*). Let us begin here. What is behind this bronze door ?

NIGHT. I think it is the Ghosts. It is long since I opened the door and since they came out.

TYLTYL (*placing the key in the lock*). I will see. (*To* BREAD) Have you the cage for the Blue Bird ?

BREAD (*with chattering teeth*). I'm not frightened, but don't you think it would be better not to open the door, but to peep through the keyhole ?

TYLTYL. I don't want your advice.

MYTYL (*suddenly beginning to cry*). I am frightened ! Where is Sugar ? I want to go home !

SUGAR (*eagerly, obsequiously*). Here I am, miss, here I am. Don't cry, I will break off one of my fingers and give you a sugar-stick.

TYLTYL. Enough of this !

(*He turns the key and cautiously opens the door. Forthwith, five or six* GHOSTS *of strange and different forms escape and disperse on every side.* BREAD, *terrified, throws away the cage and goes and hides at the back of the hall, while* NIGHT, *running after the* GHOSTS, *cries out to* TYLTYL.)

NIGHT. Quick ! Quick ! Shut the door ! They will all escape and we should never be able to catch them again ! They have felt bored in there, ever since Man ceased to take them seriously. (*She runs after the* GHOSTS,

7

TYLTYL. Yes, yes! They are huge and awful! I don't think that they have the Blue Bird.

NIGHT. You may be sure they haven't. If they had, they would eat him at once. Well, have you had enough of it? You see there is nothing to be done.

TYLTYL. I must see everything. Light said so.

NIGHT. Light said so! It's an easy thing to say when one's afraid and stays at home.

TYLTYL. Let us go to the next. What is in here?

NIGHT. This is where I lock up the Shades and the Terrors.

TYLTYL. Can I open the door?

NIGHT. Certainly. They are pretty quiet; they are like the Sicknesses.

TYLTYL (*half-opening the door, with a certain mistrustfulness, and taking a look into the cavern*). They are not there.

NIGHT (*looking into the cavern in her turn*). Well, Shades, what are you doing? Come out for a moment and stretch your legs; it will do you good. And the Terrors also. There is nothing to be afraid of. (*A few* SHADES *and a few* TERRORS, *in the shape of women shrouded, the former in black and the latter in greenish veils, piteously venture to take a few steps outside the cavern; and then, upon a movement of* TYLTYL'S, *hastily run back again.*) Come, don't be afraid. It's only a child; he won't hurt you. (*To* TYLTYL) They have become extremely timid, except the great ones, those whom you see at the back.

TYLTYL (*looking into the depths of the cave*). Oh, how frightful they look!

NIGHT. They are chained up. They are the only ones that are not afraid of Man. But shut the door, lest they should grow angry.

TYLTYL (*going to the next door*). I say! This is a darker one. What is in here?

NIGHT. There are several Mysteries behind that door. If you are absolutely bent upon it, you may open it too.

But don't go in. Be very cautious and let us get ready
to push back the door, as we did with the Wars.

TYLTYL (*half-opening the door, with unparalleled precautions, and passing his head fearsomely through the aper-
ture*). Oh! How cold! My eyes are smarting! Shut
it quickly! Push, oh, push! They are pushing against
us! (NIGHT, *the* DOG, *the* CAT *and* SUGAR *push back the
door*.) Oh, I saw!

NIGHT. What?

TYLTYL (*upset*). I don't know; it was awful! They
were all seated like monsters without eyes. Who was the
giant who tried to take hold of me?

NIGHT. It was probably Silence; he has charge of
this door. It seems to have been dreadful. You are
quite pale still and trembling all over.

TYLTYL. Yes, I would never have believed. I had
never seen. And my hands are frozen.

NIGHT. It will be much worse presently, if you go on.

TYLTYL (*going to the next door*). And this one? Is
this terrible also?

NIGHT. No; there is a little of everything here. It
is where I keep the unemployed Stars, my personal
Perfumes, a few Glimmers that belong to me, such as
Will-o'-the-Wisps, Glow-worms and Fireflies, also the
Dew, the Song of the Nightingales and so on.

TYLTYL. Just so, the Stars, the Song of the Nightingales. This must be the door.

NIGHT. Open it, if you like; there is nothing very
bad inside.

(TYLTYL *throws the door wide open. The* STARS, *in
the shape of beautiful young girls veiled in many-
coloured radiancy, escape from their prison, disperse
over the hall and form graceful groups on the steps
and around the columns, bathed in a sort of luminous penumbra. The* PERFUMES OF THE NIGHT,
who are almost invisible, the WILL-O'-THE-WISPS.

THE DOG (*panting and hiccoughing with suppressed fright*). I shall stay, I shall stay! I'm not afraid! I shall stay! I shall stay with my little god! I shall stay! I shall stay!

TYLTYL (*patting the* DOG). That's right, Tylô, that's right! Kiss me. You and I are two. And now, steady!

(*He places the key in the lock. A cry of alarm comes from the other end of the hall, where the runaways have taken refuge. The key has hardly touched the door before its tall leaves open in the middle, glide apart and disappear on either side in the thickness of the walls, suddenly revealing the most unexpected of gardens, unreal, infinite and ineffable, a dream-garden bathed in nocturnal light, where, among stars and planets, illumining all that they touch, flying ceaselessly from jewel to jewel and from moonbeam to moonbeam, fairy-like blue birds hover perpetually and harmoniously down to the confines of the horizon, birds innumerable to the point of appearing to be the breath, the azured atmosphere, the very substance of the wonderful garden.*)

TYLTYL (*dazzled, bewildered, standing in the light of the garden*). Oh! . . . Heaven! (*Turning to those who have fled*) Come quickly! They are here! It's they, it's they, it's they! We have them at last! Thousands of blue birds! Millions! Thousands of millions! There will be too many! Come, Mytyl! Come, Tylô! Come, all! Help me! (*Darting in among the birds*) You can catch them by handfuls! They are not shy! They are not afraid of us! Here! Here! (MYTYL *and the others run up. They all enter the dazzling garden, except* NIGHT *and the* CAT.) You see! There are too many of them! They fly into my hands! Look, they are eating the moonbeams! Mytyl, where are you? There are so

many blue wings, so many feathers falling that one cannot
see anything for them! Don't bite them, Tylô! Don't
hurt them! Take them very gently!

MYTYL (*covered with blue birds*). I have caught seven
already! Oh, how they flap their wings! I can't hold
them!

TYLTYL. Nor can I! I have too many of them!
They're escaping! They're coming back! Tylô has
some, too! They will drag us with them! They will
take us up to the sky! Quick, let us go out this way!
Light is waiting for us! How pleased she will be! This
way, this way!

> (*They escape from the garden, with their hands full of
> struggling birds, and, crossing the whole hall amid
> the mad whirl of the azure wings, go out on the right,
> where they first entered, followed by* BREAD *and*
> SUGAR, *who have caught no birds.* NIGHT *and
> the* CAT, *left alone, return to the back of the stage
> and look anxiously into the garden.*)

NIGHT. Haven't they got him?

THE CAT. No. I see him there, on that moonbeam.
They could not reach him, he kept too high.

> (*The* CURTAIN *falls. Immediately after, before the
> dropped curtain,* ENTER, *at the same time, on the
> left,* LIGHT *and, on the right,* TYLTYL, MYTYL *and
> the* DOG, *who run up all covered by the birds which
> they have captured. But already the birds appear
> lifeless, and, with hanging heads and drooping
> wings, are nothing more in their hands than inert
> remains.*)

LIGHT. Well, have you caught him?

TYLTYL. Yes, yes! As many as we wanted! There
are thousands of them! Here they are! Do you see

to meet the CHILDREN). Ah, there you are, my little master ! How well you look, this evening, and how handsome ! I went before you to announce your arrival. All is going well. We shall have the Blue Bird this time, I am sure. I have just sent the Rabbit to beat the troop in order to convoke the principal animals of the country. You can hear them already among the foliage. Listen ! They are a little shy and dare not come near. (*The sounds are heard of different animals, such as cows, pigs, horses, donkeys, etc. The* CAT, *aside, to* TYLTYL, *taking him apart.*) But why did you bring the Dog ? I told you he is on the worst terms with everybody, even the trees. I fear that his odious presence will spoil everything.

TYLTYL. I could not get rid of him. (*To the* DOG, *threatening him*) Go away, you ugly brute !

THE DOG. Who ? I ? Why ? What have I done ?

TYLTYL. I tell you, go away ! We don't want you here and there's an end to it. You're a nuisance, there !

THE DOG. I shan't say a word. I shall follow you at a distance. They shan't see me. Shall I sit up ?

THE CAT (*aside to* TYLTYL). Do you allow this disobedience ? Hit him on the nose with your stick ; he is really unbearable !

TYLTYL (*beating the* DOG). There, that will teach you to be more obedient !

THE DOG (*yelling*). Ow ! Ow ! Ow !

TYLTYL. What do you say to that ?

THE DOG. I must kiss you, now that you've beaten me ! (*He covers* TYLTYL *with frantic kisses and embraces.*)

TYLTYL. Come. That will do. That's enough. Go away !

MYTYL. No, no ; I want him to stay. I am afraid of everything when he is not there.

THE DOG (*leaping up and almost upsetting* MYTYL, *whom he overwhelms with hurried and enthusiastic kisses*). Oh, the dear little girl ! How beautiful she is ! How good

she is ! How beautiful she is, how sweet she is ! I must
kiss her ! Once more ! Once more ! Once more !

The Cat. What an idiot ! Well, we shall see ! Let
us lose no time. Turn the diamond.

Tyltyl. Where shall I stand ?

The Cat. In this moonbeam ; you will see better.
There, turn it gently !

> (Tyltyl *turns the Diamond. A long-drawn-out rust-*
> *ling shakes the leaves and branches. The oldest*
> *and most stately trunks open to make way for the*
> *soul which each of them contains. The appearance*
> *of these souls differs according to the appearance*
> *and character of the tree which they represent.*
> *The soul of the* Elm, *for instance, is a sort of*
> *pursy, pot-bellied, crabbed gnome ; the* Lime-
> Tree *is placid, familiar and jovial ; the* Beech,
> *elegant and agile ; the* Birch, *white, reserved*
> *and restless ; the* Willow, *stunted, dishevelled*
> *and plaintive ; the* Fir-tree, *tall, lean and*
> *taciturn ; the* Cypress, *tragic ; the* Chestnut-
> Tree, *pretentious and rather dandified ; the* Pop-
> lar, *sprightly, fussy and talkative. Some issue*
> *slowly from their trunks, torpidly stretching them-*
> *selves, as though they had been imprisoned or asleep*
> *for ages ; others leap out actively, eagerly ; and*
> *all come and stand in a circle round the two* Chil-
> dren, *while keeping as near as they can to the tree*
> *in which they were born.*)

The Poplar (*running up first and screaming at the top
of his voice*). Men ! Little men ! We shall be able to
talk to them ! We've done with silence ! Done with it !
Where do they come from ? Who are they ? What
are they ? (*To the* Lime-tree, *who comes forward quietly
smoking his pipe*) Do you know them, Daddy Lime-
tree ?

THE LIME-TREE.   I do not remember ever having seen them.

THE POPLAR.   Oh, yes, you must have !   You know all the men ; you're always hanging about their houses.

THE LIME-TREE (*examining the* CHILDREN).   No, I assure you.   I don't know them.   They are too young still.   I know only the lovers who come to see me by moonlight and the topers who drink their beer under my branches.

THE CHESTNUT-TREE (*affectedly, fixing his glass in his eye*).   Who are these ?   Are they poor people from the country ?

THE POPLAR.   Oh, as for you, Mr. Chestnut-tree, ever since you have refused to show yourself except in the streets of the big towns . . .

THE WILLOW (*hobbling along in a pair of wooden shoes*). Oh dear, oh dear !   They have come to cut off my head and arms again for faggots !

THE POPLAR.   Silence !   Here is the Oak leaving his palace !   He looks far from well this evening.   Don't you think he is growing very old ?   What can his age be ? The Fir-tree says he is four thousand ; but I am sure that he exaggerates.   Listen ; he will tell us all about it.

(*The* OAK *comes slowly forward.   He is fabulously old, crowned with mistletoe and clad in a long green gown edged with moss and lichen.   He is blind ; his white beard streams in the wind.   He leans with one hand on a knotty stick and with the other on a young* OAKLING, *who serves as his guide.   The Blue Bird is perched on his shoulder.   At his approach, the other trees draw themselves up in a row and bow respectfully.*)

TYLTYL.   He has the Blue Bird !   Quick !   Quick ! Here !   Give him to me !

THE TREES.   Silence !

THE CAT (*to* TYLTYL).   Take off your hat, it's the Oak !

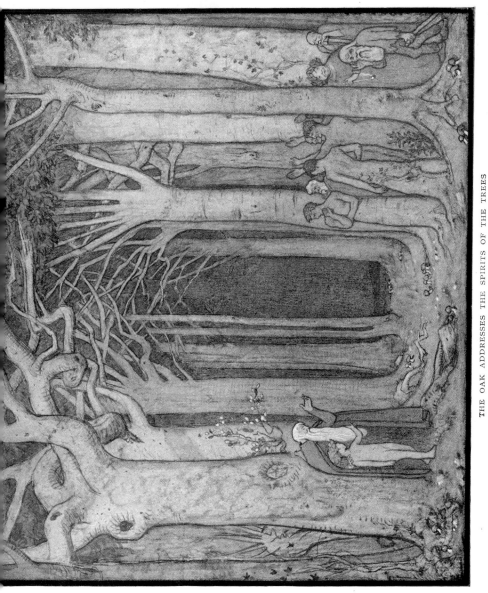

THE OAK ADDRESSES THE SPIRITS OF THE TREES

The Oak (*to* Tyltyl).   Who are you ?

Tyltyl.   I am Tyltyl, sir.   When can I have the Blue Bird ?

The Oak.   Tyltyl, the wood-cutter's son ?

Tyltyl.   Yes, sir.

The Oak.   Your father has done us much harm.   In my family alone he has put to death six hundred of my sons, four hundred and seventy-five uncles and aunts, twelve hundred cousins of both sexes, three hundred and eighty daughters-in-law, and twelve thousand great-grandsons !

Tyltyl.   I know nothing about it, sir.   He did not do it on purpose.

The Oak.   What have you come here for ; and why have you made our souls leave their abodes ?

Tyltyl.   I beg your pardon, sir, for disturbing you. The Cat said that you would tell us where the Blue Bird was.

The Oak.   Yes, I know that you are looking for the Blue Bird, that is to say, the great secret of things and of happiness, so that Man may make our servitude still harder.

Tyltyl.   Oh, no, sir ; it is for the Fairy Bérylune's little girl, who is very ill.

The Oak (*laying silence upon him with a gesture*). Enough !   I do not hear the Animals.   Where are they ? All this concerns them as much as us.   We, the Trees, must not assume the sole responsibility for the grave measures that have become necessary.   On the day when Man hears that we have done what we are about to do, there will be terrible reprisals.   It is right, therefore, that our agreement should be unanimous, so that our silence may be the same.

The Fir-tree (*looking over the top of the other trees*).   The Animals are coming.   They are following the Rabbit. Here are the souls of the Horse, the Bull, the Ox, the Cow, the Wolf, the Sheep, the Pig, the Cock, the Goat, the Ass and the Bear.

Enter the souls of the ANIMALS, *who, as the* FIR-TREE
*utters their names, come forward and sit down among
the trees, with the exception of the soul of the* GOAT,
who roams to and fro, and of the PIG, *who snuffles
among the roots.*

THE OAK. Are all here present *?*

THE RABBIT. The Hen could not leave her eggs, the
Hare had run out on an errand, the Stag has a pain in
his horns, the Fox is ill—here is the doctor's certificate—
the Goose did not understand and the Turkey flew into a
passion.

THE OAK. These abstentions are most regrettable.
However, we have a quorum. You know, my brothers, the
nature of our business. The child whom you see before
you is able, thanks to a talisman stolen from the powers
of Earth, to take possession of the Blue Bird and thus to
snatch from us the secret which we have kept since the
origin of Life. Now we know enough of Man to entertain
no doubt as to the fate which he reserves for us when he
possesses the secret. That is why it seems to me that any
hesitation would be both foolish and criminal. It is a
serious moment ; the child must be done away with
before it is too late.

TYLTYL. What is he saying ?

THE DOG (*prowling round the* OAK *and showing his fangs*).
Do you see my teeth, you old cripple ?

THE BEECH (*indignantly*). He is insulting the
Oak !

THE OAK. Is that the Dog ? Drive him out ! We
must suffer no traitors among us !

THE CAT (*aside, to* TYLTYL). Send the Dog away. It's
a misunderstanding. Leave it to me ; I will arrange things.
But send him away as quick as you can.

TYLTYL (*to the* DOG). Will you be off !

THE DOG. Do let me worry the gouty old beggar's
moss slippers ! It will be such a joke !

TYLTYL. Hold your tongue! And be off with you!
Be off, you ugly brute!

THE DOG. All right, all right, I'm going. I'll come
back when you want me.

THE CAT (*aside, to* TYLTYL). It would be a good thing
to chain him up, or he will commit some folly ; the Trees
will be angry and all will end badly.

TYLTYL. What can I do ? I have lost his leash.

THE CAT. Here's the Ivy just coming along with strong
bonds.

THE DOG (*growling*). I'll come back, I'll come back!
Ugh! Goutytoes! Timbertoes! Pack of old stunted
growths, pack of old roots! It's the Cat who's at the
bottom of all this! I'll be even with her! What have
you been whispering about, you sneak, you tigress, you
Judas! Wow, wow, wow!

THE CAT. You see, he insults everybody.

TYLTYL. Yes, he is unbearable and one can't hear
one's self speak. Mr. Ivy, will you chain him up,
please ?

THE IVY (*timorously going up to the* DOG). Won't he
bite ?

THE DOG (*growling*). On the contrary, on the contrary !
He's going to kiss you ! Just you wait and see ! Come
along, come along, you old ball of twine, you !

TYLTYL (*threatening him with his stick*). Tylô !

THE DOG (*cringing at* TYLTYL's *feet and wagging his
tail*). What am I to do, my little god ?

TYLTYL. Lie down flat ! Obey the Ivy. Let him
bind you, or . . .

THE DOG (*growling between his teeth, while the* IVY *binds
him*). Ball of twine ! Hunk of yarn ! Hangman's rope !
Calves' leash ! Look, my little god ! He's cutting my
paws ! He's choking me !

TYLTYL. I don't care ! It's your own fault. Hold
your tongue ; be quiet ; you're unbearable !

THE DOG. You're wrong, for all that. They mean

9

mischief.   Take care, my little god !   He's closing my mouth !   I can't speak !

THE IVY (*who has tied up the* DOG *like a parcel*).   Where shall we put him ?   I've muzzled him finely.   He can't utter a word.

THE OAK.   Fasten him tight down there, behind my trunk, to my big root.   We will decide later what had best be done with him.

(*The* IVY *and the* POPLAR *carry the* DOG *behind the* OAK's *trunk.*)

THE OAK.   Is that done ?   Well, now that we are rid of that inconvenient witness, of that renegade, let us delibe- rate in accordance with justice and truth.   I will not conceal from you the deep and painful nature of my emotion. This is the first time that it is given to us to judge Man and make him feel our power.   I do not think that, after the harm which he has done us, after the monstrous in- justice which we have suffered, there can remain the least doubt as to the sentence that awaits him.

ALL THE TREES *and* ALL THE ANIMALS.   No !   No !   No ! No doubt at all !   Hanging !   Death !   The injustice has been too great !   The abuse too wicked !   It has lasted too long !   Crush him !   Eat him !   At once !   At once !

TYLTYL (*to the* CAT).   What is the matter with them ? Are they displeased ?

THE CAT.   Don't be alarmed.   They are a little angry because spring is late.   Leave it to me ; I will settle all that.

THE OAK.   This unanimity was inevitable.   We must now decide, in order to avoid reprisals, which form of execution will be the most practical, the easiest, the quickest and the safest, which will leave the fewest accusing traces when Man finds the little bodies in the forest.

TYLTYL.   What is all this about ?   What is he driving

at ? I am getting tired of this.   He has the Blue Bird ;
let him hand it over.

THE BULL (*coming forward*).   The most practical and
the surest way is a good butt with the horns in the pit of
the stomach.   Shall I go at him ?

THE OAK.   Who speaks ?

THE CAT.   It's the Bull.

THE COW.   It would be better to keep quiet.   I won't
meddle with it.   I have to browse all the grass in the field
which you can see down there, in the blue light of the moon.
I have too much to do.

THE OX.   I also.   However, I agree to everything
beforehand.

THE BEECH.   I offer my highest branch to hang them
on.

THE IVY.   And I the slip-knot.

THE FIR-TREE.   And I the four planks for their little
coffin.

THE CYPRESS.   And I a perpetual grant of a tomb.

THE WILLOW.   The simplest way would be to drown
them in one of my rivers.   I will take charge of that.

THE LIME-TREE (*in a conciliatory tone*).   Come, come !
Is it really necessary to go to such extremities ?   They
are very young still.   We could simply prevent them
from doing harm by keeping them prisoners in an enclosure
which I will undertake to form by planting myself all
around.

THE OAK.   Who speaks ?   I seem to recognize the
honeyed accents of the Lime-tree.

THE FIR-TREE.   Yes, it's he.

THE OAK.   So there is a renegade among us, as among
the Animals ?   Hitherto we have only had to deplore
the disloyalty of the Fruit-trees ; but they are not real
trees.

THE PIG (*rolling his greedy little eyes*).   I think we should
first eat the little girl.   She ought to be very tender.

TYLTYL.   What's he saying ?   Just wait a bit, you . . .

THE CAT. I don't know what is the matter with them ; but things are beginning to look badly.

THE OAK. Silence ! What we have to decide is which of us shall have the honour of striking the first blow, who shall ward off from our tops the greatest danger that has threatened us since the birth of Man.

THE FIR-TREE. That honour falls to you, our king and our patriarch.

THE OAK. Is that the Fir-tree speaking ? Alas, I am too old ! I am blind and infirm and my numbed arms no longer obey me. No, to you, brother, ever green, ever upright, to you, who have witnessed the birth of most of these trees, to you be the glory, in default of myself, of the noble act of our deliverance.

THE FIR-TREE. I thank you, venerable father. But, as I shall, in any case, have the honour of burying the two victims, I should be afraid of arousing the just jealousy of my fellows ; and I think that, next to ourselves, the oldest and the worthiest and the one that owns the best club is the Beech.

THE BEECH. You know I am worm-eaten and my club is no longer to be relied upon. But the Elm and the Cypress have powerful weapons.

THE ELM. I should be only too pleased ; but I can hardly stand upright. A mole twisted my great toe last night.

THE CYPRESS. As for me, I am ready. But, like my brother, the Fir-tree, I shall have, if not the privilege of burying them, at least the advantage of weeping over their tomb. It would be an unlawful plurality of offices. Ask the Poplar.

THE POPLAR. Me ? Are you serious ? Why, my wood is more tender than the flesh of a child ! And, besides, I don't know what's the matter with me. I am shivering with fever. Just look at my leaves. I must have caught cold at sunrise this morning.

THE OAK (*bursting with indignation*). You are afraid

of Man ! Even these unprotected and unarmed little
children inspire you with the mysterious terror which has
always made us the slaves that we are ! No ! Enough
of this ! Things being as they are and the opportunity
unequalled, I shall go forth alone, old, crippled, trembling,
blind as I am, against the hereditary enemy ! Where is
he ?

(*Groping with his stick, he moves towards* TYLTYL.)

TYLTYL (*taking his knife from his pocket*). Is it me
he's after, that old one, with his big stick ?

ALL THE TREES (*uttering a cry of alarm at the sight of
the knife, they step in between and hold back the* OAK). The
knife ! Take care ! The knife !

THE OAK (*struggling*). Let me be ! What does it
matter ? The knife or the axe ! Who's holding me back ?
What ! You are all here ? What ! You all want to . . .
(*Flinging down his stick*) Well, so be it ! Shame upon us !
Let the animals deliver us !

THE BULL. That's right ! I'll see to it ! And with
one blow of the horns !

THE OX *and* THE COW (*holding him back by the tail*).
What are you doing ? Don't be a fool ! It's a bad busi-
ness ! It will end badly. It is we who will pay for it.
Do let be. It's the Wild Animals' business.

THE BULL. No, no ! It's my business ! Wait and
see ! Look here, hold me back or there will be an
accident !

TYLTYL (*to* MYTYL, *who is uttering piercing screams*).
Don't be afraid ! Stand behind me. I have my
knife.

THE COCK. He has plenty of pluck, the little chap !

TYLTYL. So you've made up your minds, it's me you're
going for ?

THE ASS. Why, of course, my little man ; you've
taken long enough to see it !

jump at his throat. Ow! That's a kick. The Ass has broken two of my teeth.

TYLTYL. I'm done for, Tylô! Ah! That was a blow from the Elm. Look, my hand's bleeding. That's the Wolf or the Pig.

THE DOG. Wait, my little god. Let me kiss you. There, a gook lick. That will do you good. Keep behind me. They dare not come again. Yes, though! Here they are coming back! This time it's serious! We must stand firm!

TYLTYL (*dropping to the ground*). No, I can hold out no longer!

THE DOG (*listening*). They are coming! I hear them. I scent them!

TYLTYL. Where? Who?

THE DOG. There! There! It's Light! She has found us! Saved, my little king! Kiss me! We are saved! Look! They're alarmed! They're retreating! They're afraid!

TYLTYL. Light! Light! Come quick! Hurry! They have rebelled! They are all against us!

Enter LIGHT. *As she comes forward, the dawn rises over the forest, which becomes light.*

LIGHT. What is it? What has happened? But, my poor boy, didn't you know? Turn the diamond! They will return into silence and obscurity; and you will no longer perceive their hidden feelings.

(TYLTYL *turns the diamond. Immediately, the souls of all the* TREES *rush back into the trunks, which close upon them. The souls of the* ANIMALS *also disappear; and a* COW *and a* SHEEP, *etc., are seen peacefully browsing in the distance. The forest becomes harmless once more.* TYLTYL *looks around him in amazement.*)

TYLTYL. Where are they ? What was the matter with them ? Were they mad ?

LIGHT. No, they are always like that ; but we do not know it, because we do not see it. I told you so before : it is dangerous to rouse them when I am not there.

TYLTYL (*wiping his knife*). Well, but for the Dog . . . and if I had not had my knife ! . . . I would never have believed that they were so wicked !

LIGHT. You see that Man is all alone against all, in this world.

THE DOG. Are you very badly hurt, my little god ?

TYLTYL. Nothing serious. As for Mytyl, they have not touched her. But you, my dear Tylô ? Your mouth is all over blood and your paw is broken !

THE DOG. Nothing worth speaking of. It won't show to-morrow. But it was a tough fight !

THE CAT (*appearing from behind a thicket limping*). I should think it was ! The Ox caught me a blow with his horns in the stomach. You can't see the marks, but it's very painful. And the Oak broke my paw.

THE DOG. I should like to know which one.

MYTYL (*stroking the* CAT). My poor Tylette, did he really ? Where were you ? I did not see you.

THE CAT (*hypocritically*). Mummy dear, I was wounded at the first, while attacking that horrid Pig, who wanted to eat you. And then the Oak gave me a great blow which struck me senseless.

THE DOG (*to the* CAT, *between his teeth*). As for you, I want a word with you. It will keep, though !

THE CAT (*plaintively to* MYTYL). Mummy dear, he's insulting me. He wants to hurt me.

MYTYL (*to the* DOG). Leave him alone, will you, you ugly beast ?

(*They* ALL *go out.*)

CURTAIN

10

ACT IV

SCENE I. *Before the Curtain*

Enter TYLTYL, MYTYL, LIGHT, *the* DOG, *the* CAT, BREAD,
FIRE, SUGAR, WATER *and* MILK.

LIGHT. I have received a note from the Fairy Bérylune
telling me that the Blue Bird is probably here.

TYLTYL. Where ?

LIGHT. Here, in the graveyard behind this wall. It
appears that one of the Dead in the graveyard is hiding
it in his tomb. We must find out which one it is. We
shall have to pass them under review.

TYLTYL. Under review ? How is that done ?

LIGHT. It is very simple ; at midnight, so as not to
disturb them too greatly, you will turn the diamond.
You will see them come out of the ground ; or else you
will see those who do not come out lying in their tombs.

TYLTYL. Will they not be angry ?

LIGHT. Not at all ; they will not even know. They do
not like being disturbed, but, as it is their custom, in any
case, to come out at midnight, that will not inconvenience
them.

TYLTYL. Why are Bread and Sugar and Milk so pale ;
and why do they say nothing ?

MILK (*staggering*). I feel I am going to turn.

LIGHT (*aside, to* TYLTYL). Do not mind them. They
are afraid of the Dead.

FIRE (*frisking about*). I'm not afraid of them ! I
am used to burning them. Time was when I burnt them
all ; that was much better fun than nowadays.

THE GRAVEYARD

TYLTYL.   And why is Tylô trembling ? Is he afraid, too ?

THE DOG.   I ? I'm not trembling ! I am never afraid ; but, if you went away, I should go too.

TYLTYL.   And has the Cat nothing to say ?

THE CAT (*mysteriously*).   I know what's what.

TYLTYL (*to* LIGHT).   Are you coming with us ?

LIGHT.   No ; it is better that I should remain at the gate of the graveyard with the Things and the Animals. The hour has not come. Light cannot penetrate yet among the Dead. I shall leave you alone with Mytyl.

TYLTYL.   And may not Tylô stay with us ?

THE DOG.   Yes, yes, I shall stay, I shall stay here ! I want to stay with my little god !

LIGHT.   It is impossible. The Fairy gave formal orders ; besides, there is nothing to fear.

THE DOG.   Very well, very well, it makes no difference. If they are vicious, my little god, all you have to do is this (*he whistles*) and you shall see. It will be just as in the forest : wow ! Wow ! Wow !

LIGHT.   Come, good-bye, dear children. I shall not be far away. (*She kisses the* CHILDREN.) Those who love me and whom I love always find me again. (*To the* THINGS *and the* ANIMALS) This way, all of you.

(*She goes out with the* THINGS *and the* ANIMALS. *The* CHILDREN *remain alone in the middle of the stage. The curtain opens and discloses the next scene.*)

SCENE II. *The Graveyard*

It is night. The moon is shining on a country graveyard. Numerous tombstones, grassy mounds, wooden crosses, stone slabs, etc. TYLTYL and MYTYL are standing by a short stone pillar.

MYTYL. I am frightened!

TYLTYL (*not too much at his ease*). I am never frightened.

MYTYL. I say, are the Dead wicked?

TYLTYL. Why, no, they're not alive!

MYTYL. Have you ever seen one?

TYLTYL. Yes, once, long ago, when I was very young.

MYTYL. I say, what was it like?

TYLTYL. Quite white, very still and very cold, and it didn't talk.

MYTYL. I say, are we going to see them?

TYLTYL. Why, of course, Light promised we should.

MYTYL. Where are the Dead?

TYLTYL. Here, under the grass or under those big stones.

MYTYL. Are they there all the year round?

TYLTYL. Yes.

MYTYL (*pointing to the slabs*). Are those the doors of their houses?

TYLTYL. Yes.

MYTYL. Do they go out when it's fine?

TYLTYL. They can only go out at night.

MYTYL. Why?

TYLTYL. Because they are in their shirts.

MYTYL. Do they go out also when it rains?

TYLTYL. When it rains, they stay at home.

MYTYL. I say, is it nice in their homes?

TYLTYL. I hear it's very cramped.

MYTYL. Have they any little children?

TYLTYL. Why, yes; they have all those which die.

MYTYL. And what do they live on?

TYLTYL. They eat roots.

MYTYL. Shall we see them?

TYLTYL. Of course; we see everything when I turn the diamond.

MYTYL. And what will they say?

TYLTYL. They will say nothing, because they don't talk.

Mytyl.   Why don't they talk ?

Tyltyl.   Because they have nothing to say.

Mytyl.   Why have they nothing to say ?

Tyltyl.   You're a nuisance.   (*A pause.*)

Mytyl.   When will you turn the diamond ?

Tyltyl.   You heard Light say that I was to wait until midnight, because that disturbs them less.

Mytyl.   Why does that disturb them less ?

Tyltyl.   Because that is when they go out to take the air.

Mytyl.   Is it not midnight yet ?

Tyltyl.   Do you see the church clock ?

Mytyl.   Yes, I can even see the small hand.

Tyltyl.   Well, midnight is just going to strike.   There ! Do you hear ?

(The clock strikes twelve.)

Mytyl.   I want to go away !

Tyltyl.   Not now.   I am going to turn the diamond.

Mytyl.   No, no ! Don't ! I want to go away ! I am so frightened, little brother.   I am terribly frightened !

Tyltyl.   But there is no danger.

Mytyl.   I don't want to see the Dead !   I don't want to see them !

Tyltyl.   Very well, you shall not see them ; shut your eyes.

Mytyl (*clinging to* Tyltyl's *clothes*).   Tyltyl, I can't stay !   No, I can't possibly !   They are going to come out of the ground !

Tyltyl.   Don't tremble like that.   They will only come out for a moment.

Mytyl.   But you're trembling, too !   They will be awful !

Tyltyl.   It is time, the hour is passing.

(Tyltyl *turns the diamond. A terrifying minute*

of silence and motionlessness elapses, after which, slowly, the crosses totter, the mounds open, the slabs are raised.)

MYTYL (*cowering against* TYLTYL). They are coming out! They are there!

(Then, from all the gaping tombs, there rises gradually an efflorescence at first frail and timid, like steam; then white and virginal and more and more tufty, more and more tall and plentiful and marvellous. Little by little, irresistibly, invading all things, it transforms the graveyard into a sort of fairy-like and nuptial garden, over which rise the first rays of the dawn. The dew glitters, the flowers open their blooms, the wind murmurs in the leaves, the bees hum, the birds wake and flood the air with the first raptures of their hymns to the sun and to life. Stunned and dazzled, TYLTYL and MYTYL, holding each other by the hand, take a few steps among the flowers while they seek for the trace of the tombs.)

MYTYL (*looking in the grass*). Where are the Dead?
TYLTYL (*also looking*). There are no Dead.

CURTAIN

SCENE III. *Before the Curtain*

The curtain represents beautiful clouds.

Enter TYLTYL, MYTYL, LIGHT, *the* DOG, *the* CAT. BREAD, FIRE, SUGAR, WATER *and* MILK.

TYLTYL TURNS THE DIAMOND

LIGHT. I believe we have the Blue Bird this time. I ought to have thought of it at first. But the idea came to me, like a ray from the sky, this morning only, when I recovered my strength in the dawn. We are at the entrance to the enchanted gardens where all Man's Joys, all Man's Happinesses are gathered together in the charge of Fate.

TYLTYL. Are there many of them ? Shall we have any ? Are they little ?

LIGHT. Some are little and some are great ; some are coarse and some are delicate ; some are very beautiful and others not so pleasant to look upon. But the ugliest were expelled from the gardens some time ago and took refuge with the Miseries. For we must not forget that the Miseries inhabit an adjoining cave, which communicates with the Garden of Happiness and is separated from it only by a sort of vapour or fine veil, lifted at every moment by the winds that blow from the heights of Justice or from the depths of Eternity. What we have now to do is to organize ourselves and take certain precautions. Generally, the Joys are very good ; but, still, there are some of them that are more dangerous and treacherous than the greatest Miseries.

BREAD. I have an idea ! If they are dangerous and treacherous, would it not be better for us all to wait at the door, so that we may lend a hand to the children should they be obliged to fly ?

THE DOG. Not at all ! Not at all ! I mean to go everywhere with my little gods ! Let those who are afraid remain at the door ! We have no need (*looking at* BREAD) of cowards, (*looking at the* CAT) or traitors !

FIRE. I shall go ! I hear it's great fun ! They dance all the time.

BREAD. Do they eat as well ?

WATER (*moaning*). I have never known the smallest Happiness ! I should like to see some at last !

LIGHT. Hold your tongues ! Who asked your opinions ?

This is what I have decided : the Dog, Bread and Sugar shall go with the children. Water shall stay outside, because she is too cold, and Fire, because he is too turbulent. I strongly urge Milk to remain at the door, because she is so impressionable. As for the Cat, she can please herself.

THE DOG. She's afraid !

THE CAT. I shall take the opportunity of calling on some Miseries who are old friends of mine and who live next door to the Joys.

TYLTYL. And you, Light ? Aren't you coming ?

LIGHT. I cannot go into the Joys, like this : most of them cannot endure me. But I have here the thick veil with which I cover myself when I visit happy people. (*She unfolds a long veil and wraps herself in it carefully.*) Not a ray of my soul must startle them, for there are many Happinesses that are afraid and are not happy. There ; like this, even the ugliest and coarsest of them will have nothing to fear.

(*The* CURTAIN *opens and discloses the next Scene.*)

SCENE IV. *The Gardens of Happiness*

When the curtain opens, the stage represents, in the front of the gardens, a sort of hall formed of tall marble columns, between which hang heavy purple draperies, supported by golden ropes and concealing all the background. The architecture suggests the most sensual and sumptuous moments of the Venetian or Flemish Renascence, as seen in the pictures of Veronese or Rubens, with garlands, horns of plenty, fringes, vases, statues, gildings, lavishly distributed on every side. In the middle stands a massive and marvellous table of jasper and silver-gilt, laden with candlesticks, glass, gold and silver plate and fabulous viands. Around the table, the biggest Luxuries *of the Earth sit eating, drinking, shouting, singing, tossing and lolling about or sleeping among the haunches of venison, the miraculous fruits, the overturned jars and ewers. They are enormously, incredibly fat and red in the face, covered with velvet and brocade, crowned with gold and pearls and precious stones. Beautiful female slaves incessantly bring decorated dishes and foaming beverages. Vulgar, blatantly hilarious music, in which the brasses predominate. The stage is bathed in a red and heavy light.*

(Tyltyl, Mytyl, *the* Dog, Bread *and* Sugar *are a little awestruck at first and crowd round* Light *in the foreground, to the right. The* Cat, *without a word, walks to the background, also to the right, lifts a dark curtain and disappears.*)

Tyltyl.   Who are those fat gentlemen enjoying themselves and eating such a lot of good things ?

Light.   They are the biggest Luxuries of the Earth, the ones that can be seen with the naked eye. It is possible, though not very likely, that the Blue Bird may have strayed among them for a moment. That is why you must not turn the diamond yet. For form's sake, we will begin by searching this part of the hall.

Tyltyl.   Can we go near them ?

Light.   Certainly. They are not ill-natured, though they are vulgar and usually rather ill-bred.

Mytyl.   What lovely cakes they have !

The Dog.   And game ! And sausages ! And legs of lamb and calves' liver ! (*Proclaiming*) There's nothing better or nicer or lovelier in the world than calves' liver !

Bread.   Except quartern-loaves made of fine white flour ! They have beauties ! How lovely they are ! How lovely they are ! They are bigger than I am !

SUGAR.   I beg your pardon, I beg your pardon, I beg a thousand pardons.   Allow me, allow me.   I would not like to hurt anybody's feelings ; but are you not forgetting the sweetmeats, which form the glory of that table and which, if I may say so, surpass in grandeur and magnificence all that exists in this hall, or perhaps anywhere else ?

TYLTYL.   How pleased and happy they look ! And they are shouting ! And laughing ! And singing !   I believe they have seen us.

> (*A dozen of the biggest* LUXURIES *have risen from table and now, holding their stomachs in their hands, come waddling towards the* CHILDREN.)

LIGHT.   Have no fear, they are very affable.   They will probably invite you to dinner.   Do not accept, do not accept anything, lest you forget your mission.

TYLTYL.   What ?   Not even a tiny cake ?   They look so good, so fresh, so well iced with sugar, covered with candied fruits and brimming over with cream !

LIGHT.   They are dangerous and would break your will. A man should know how to sacrifice something to the duty he is performing.   Refuse politely, but firmly.   Here they come.

THE BIGGEST OF THE LUXURIES (*holding out his hand to* TYLTYL).   How do you do, Tyltyl ?

TYLTYL (*surprised*).   Why, do you know me ?   Who are you ?

THE LUXURY.   I am the biggest of the Luxuries, the Luxury of Being Rich ; and I come, in the name of my brothers, to beg you and your family to honour our endless repast with your presence.   You will find yourself surrounded by all that is best among the real, big Luxuries of this Earth.   Allow me to introduce to you the chief of them.   Here is my son-in-law, the Luxury of Being a Landowner, who has a stomach shaped like a pear.   This

The inscription on the pedestal reads:

BREVIS·ILL
VOLUPTAS
ABROGAT
ÆTERNUM
CŒLI
DECUS

THE CHILDREN ENTER THE PALACE OF THE LUXURIES

is the Luxury of Satisfied Vanity, who has such a nice, puffy face. (*The* LUXURY OF SATISFIED VANITY *gives a patronizing nod.*) These are the Luxury of Drinking when you are not Thirsty and the Luxury of Eating when you are not Hungry : they are twins ; and their legs are made of macaroni. (*They bow, staggering.*) Here are the Luxury of Knowing Nothing, who is as deaf as a post, and the Luxury of Understanding Nothing, who is as blind as a bat. Here are the Luxury of Doing Nothing and the Luxury of Sleeping more than Necessary : their hands are made of breadcrumb and their eyes of peach-jelly. Lastly, here is Fat Laughter : his mouth is split from ear to ear and he is irresistible. (FAT LAUGHTER *bows, writhing and holding his sides.*)

TYLTYL (*pointing to a* LUXURY *who is standing a little on one side*). And who is that one, who dares not come up to us and who is turning his back ?

THE LUXURY OF BEING RICH. Do not ask about him : he is a little awkward and is not fit to be introduced to children. (*Seizing* TYLTYL'S *hands*) But come along ! They are beginning the banquet all over again. It is the twelfth time since this morning. We are only waiting for you. Do you hear all the revellers calling and shouting for you ? I cannot introduce all of them to you, there are so many of them. (*Offering his arm to the two* CHILDREN) Allow me to lead you to the two seats of honour.

TYLTYL. No, thank you very much, Mr. Luxury. I am so sorry. I can't come for the moment. We are in a great hurry, we are looking for the Blue Bird. You don't happen, I suppose, to know where he is hiding ?

THE LUXURY. The Blue Bird ? Wait a bit. Yes, yes, I remember. Someone was telling me about him the other day. He is a bird that is not good to eat, I believe. At any rate, he has never figured on our table. That means that we have a poor opinion of him. But don't trouble ; we have plenty of much better things. You shall share our life, you shall see all that we do.

TYLTYL. What do you do ?

THE LUXURY. Why, we occupy ourselves incessantly in doing nothing. We never have a moment's rest. We have to drink, we have to eat, we have to sleep. It's most engrossing.

TYLTYL. Is it amusing ?

THE LUXURY. Why, yes. It needs must be ; it's all there is on this Earth.

LIGHT. Do you think so ?

THE LUXURY (*pointing to* LIGHT, *aside, to* TYLTYL). Who is that ill-bred young person ?

(*During the whole of the preceding conversation, a crowd of* LUXURIES *of the second order have been busying themselves with the* DOG, SUGAR *and* BREAD *and have dragged them to the orgy.* TYLTYL *suddenly sees them seated fraternally at the table with their hosts, eating, drinking and flinging themselves about wildly.*)

TYLTYL. Why, look, Light ! They are sitting at the table !

LIGHT. Call them back, or this will have a bad end !

TYLTYL. Tylô ! Here, Tylô ! Come here at once, will you ? Do you hear ? And you two, Sugar and Bread, who told you to leave me ? What are you doing there, without permission ?

BREAD (*speaking with his mouth full*). Can't you keep a civil tongue in your head ?

TYLTYL. What ! Is Bread daring to be impertinent ? Why, what's come over you ? And you, Tylô ! Is that the way to obey ? Now then, come here, on your knees, on your knees ! And look sharp about it !

THE DOG (*muttering, from the end of the table*). When I'm eating, I'm at home to nobody and I hear nothing.

SUGAR (*honey-mouthed*). Pardon us, we could not

possibly leave such charming hosts so abruptly ; they
would be offended.

The Luxury. You see! They are setting you an
example. Come, we are waiting for you. We won't hear
of a refusal. We shall have to resort to a gentle violence.
Come, Luxuries, help me! Let us push them to the
table by force, so that they may be happy in spite of
themselves! (*All the* Luxuries, *uttering cries of joy and
skipping about as nimbly as they are able, drag the* Children,
who struggle, while Fat Laughter *seizes* Light *vigorously
round the waist.*)

Light. Turn the diamond, it is time!

> (Tyltyl *obeys* Light's *order. Forthwith the stage is
> lit up with an ineffably pure, divinely roseate,
> harmonious and ethereal brightness. The heavy
> ornaments in the foreground, the thick red hang-
> ings become unfastened and disappear, revealing
> a fabulous and smiling garden of blithe peace and
> serenity, a sort of verdant palace of harmonious
> perspectives, in which the magnificence of the
> mighty, luminous, exuberant and yet trained
> foliage and the virginal gaiety of the flowers and the
> cool gladness of the waters that flow, stream and
> spurt on every side seem to carry the idea of felicity
> to the very confines of the horizon. The table of
> the orgy melts away, without leaving a trace ;
> the velvets, the brocades, the garlands of the*
> Luxuries *rise before the luminous gust that
> pervades the scene, tear asunder and fall, together
> with the grinning masks, at the feet of the astounded
> revellers. These become visibly deflated, like burst
> bladders, exchange glances, blink their eyes in the
> unknown rays that hurt them ; and, seeing them-
> selves at last as they really are, that is to say, naked,
> hideous, flabby and lamentable, they begin to utter
> yells of shame and dismay, amid which those of*

FAT LAUGHTER *are clearly distinguishable above all the rest. The* LUXURY OF UNDERSTANDING NOTHING *alone remains perfectly calm, while his friends rush about madly, trying to flee, to hide themselves in corners which they hope to find dark. But there is no shadow in the dazzling garden. And so the majority, in their despair, decide to pass through the threatening curtain which, in an angle on the right, closes the vault of the Cave of the Miseries. Each time that one of them, in his panic, raises a skirt of the curtain, a storm of oaths, imprecations and maledictions is heard to issue from the hollow depths of the cave. As for the* DOG, BREAD *and* SUGAR, *they hang their heads, join the group of the* CHILDREN *and hide behind them very sheepishly.*)

TYLTYL (*watching the* LUXURIES *flying*).   Goodness, how ugly they are!   Where are they going?

LIGHT.   I really believe that they have lost their heads. They are going to take refuge with the Miseries, where I very much fear that they will be kept for good.

TYLTYL (*looking around him, wonderstruck*).   Oh, what a beautiful garden, what a beautiful garden!   Where are we?

LIGHT.   We have not moved: it is your eyes that have changed their sphere.   We now behold the truth of things; and we shall soon perceive the soul of the Joys that endure the brightness of the diamond.

TYLTYL.   How beautiful it is!   And what lovely weather!   It is just like midsummer.   Hullo!   It looks as though people were coming to talk to us.

(*The gardens begin to fill with angel forms that seem to be emerging from a long slumber and glide harmoniously between the trees. They are clad in shimmering dresses, of soft and subtle shades:*

rose-awakening, water's-smile, blue-of-dawn, amber-
dew, etc.)

LIGHT. Here come some amiable and curious Joys
who will direct us.

TYLTYL. Do you know them?

LIGHT. Yes, I know them all; I often come to them,
without their knowing who I am.

TYLTYL. Oh, what a lot of them there are! They are
crowding from every side.

LIGHT. There were many more of them once. The
Luxuries have done them great harm.

TYLTYL. No matter, there are a good few of them left.

LIGHT. You will see plenty of others, as the influence
of the diamond spreads through the gardens. There are
many more Happinesses on Earth than people think;
but the generality of men do not discover them.

TYLTYL. Here are some little ones: let us run and
meet them.

LIGHT. It is unnecessary: those which interest us
will pass this way. We have no time to make the acquaint-
ance of all the rest.

(*A troop of* LITTLE HAPPINESSES, *frisking and bursting
with laughter, run up out of the foliage at the back
and dance round the* CHILDREN *in a ring.*)

TYLTYL. How pretty, how very pretty they are!
Where do they come from? who are they?

LIGHT. They are the Children's Happinesses.

TYLTYL. Can one speak to them?

LIGHT. It would be no use. They sing, they dance,
they laugh, but they do not talk yet.

TYLTYL (*skipping about*). How do you do? How
do you do? Oh, look at that fat one laughing! What
pretty cheeks they have, what pretty frocks they have!
Are they all rich here?

LIGHT. Why, no. Here, as everywhere, there are many more poor than rich.

TYLTYL. Where are the poor ones?

LIGHT. You can't distinguish them. A Child's Happiness is always arrayed in all that is most beautiful in Heaven and upon Earth.

TYLTYL (*unable to restrain himself*). I should love to dance with them.

LIGHT. It is absolutely impossible, we have no time. I see that they have not the Blue Bird. Besides, they are in a hurry: you see, they have already passed. They too have no time to waste, for childhood is very short.

(*Another troop of* HAPPINESSES, *a little taller than the last, rush into the hall, singing at the top of their voice, " There they are! There they are! They see us! They see us!" and dance a merry fling around the* CHILDREN, *at the end of which the one who appears to be the chief of the little band goes up to* TYLTYL *with hand outstretched.*)

THE HAPPINESS. How do you do, Tyltyl?

TYLTYL. Another one who knows me! (*To* LIGHT) I am getting known wherever I go! (*To the* HAPPINESS) Who are you?

THE HAPPINESS. Don't you recognize me? I'll wager that you don't recognize anyone here!

TYLTYL (*a little embarrassed*). Why, no. I don't know . . . I don't remember seeing any of you.

THE HAPPINESS. There, do you hear? I was sure of it! He has never seen us! (*All the other* HAPPINESSES *burst out laughing.*) Why, my dear Tyltyl, we are the only things you do know! We are always around you. We eat, drink, wake up, breathe and live with you!

TYLTYL. Oh, yes, just so, I know, I remember. But I should like to know what your names are.

THE HAPPINESS. I can see that you know nothing.
I am the chief Happiness of your home ; and all these are
the other Happinesses that fill it.

TYLTYL.   Then there are Happinesses in my home ?

(*All the* HAPPINESSES *burst out laughing.*)

THE HAPPINESS. You heard him ! Are there Happinesses in your home ! Why, you little wretch, it is
crammed with Happinesses in every nook and cranny !
We laugh, we sing, we create enough joy to knock down
the walls and lift the roof ; but, do what we may, you see
nothing and you hear nothing. I hope that in future, you
will be a little more sensible. Meantime, you shall shake
hands with the more noteworthy of us. Then, when you
go home again, you will recognize them more easily and
at the end of a fine day, you will know how to encourage
them with a smile, to thank them with a pleasant word,
for they really do all they can to make your life easy and
delightful. Let me introduce myself first : the Happiness of Being Well, at your service. I am not the prettiest,
but I am the most important. Will you know me again ?
This is the Happiness of Pure Air, who is almost transparent. Here is the Happiness of Loving One's Parents,
who is clad in grey and always a little sad, because no one
ever looks at him. Here are the Happiness of the Blue
Sky, who, of course, is dressed in blue, and the Happiness
of the Forest, who, also of course, is clad in green : you
will see him every time you go to the window. Here,
again, is the good Happiness of Sunny Hours, who is
diamond-coloured ; and this is the Happiness of Spring,
who is bright emerald.

TYLTYL.   And are you as fine as that every day ?

THE HAPPINESS OF BEING WELL.   Why, yes, it is
Sunday every day, in every house, when people open their
eyes. And then, when evening comes, here is the Happiness of the Sunsets, who is grander than all the kings in

12

I am too young; I have never seen her smile yet. Behind her is the Joy of Being Good, who is the happiest, but the saddest; and it is very difficult to keep her from going to the Miseries, whom she would like to console. On the right is the Joy of Work Accomplished, next to the Joy of Thinking. After her comes the Joy of Understanding, who is always looking for her brother, the Luxury of Understanding Nothing.

TYLTYL. But I have seen her brother! He went to the Miseries with the Big Luxuries.

THE HAPPINESS. I was certain of it. He has turned out badly; keeping evil company has corrupted him entirely. But do not speak of it to his sister. She would want to go and look for him and we should lose one of our most beautiful Joys. Here again, among the greatest Joys, is the Joy of Seeing what is Beautiful, who daily adds a few rays to the light that reigns amongst us.

TYLTYL. And there, far away, far away, in the golden clouds, the one whom I can hardly see when I stand as high as I can on tip-toe?

THE HAPPINESS. That is the Great Joy of Loving. But, do what you will, you are much too small to see her altogether.

TYLTYL. And over there, right at the back, those who are veiled and who do not come near?

THE HAPPINESS. Those are the Joys whom men do not yet know.

TYLTYL. What are the others doing? Why do they stand aside?

THE HAPPINESS. It is before a new Joy who is arriving, perhaps the purest that we have here.

TYLTYL. Who is it?

THE HAPPINESS. Don't you recognize her yet? But take a better look at her, open your two eyes down to the very heart of your soul! She has seen you, she has seen you! She runs up to you, holding out her arms! It is your mother's Joy, it is the peerless Joy of Maternal Love!

MOTHERHOOD ENTHRONED

(*The other* Joys, *who have hastened up from every side, fall back in silence before the* Joy of Maternal Love.)

The Joy of Maternal Love. Tyltyl! And Mytyl! What, do I find you here?   I never expected it!   I was very lonely at home; and here are you two climbing to that Heaven where the souls of all mothers beam with joy!   But first kisses, heaps and heaps of kisses!   Into my arms, the two of you; there is nothing on earth that gives greater happiness!   Tyltyl, aren't you laughing? Nor you either, Mytyl?   Don't you know your mother's love when you see it?   Why, look at me: are these not my eyes, my lips, my arms?

Tyltyl.   Yes, yes, I recognize them, but I did not know.   You are like Mummy, but you are much prettier.

Maternal Love. Why, of course, I have stopped growing old.   And every day brings me fresh strength and youth and happiness.   Each of your smiles makes me younger by a year.   At home, that does not show; but here everything is seen and it is the truth.

Tyltyl (*wonderstruck, gazing at her and kissing her by turns*).   And that beautiful dress of yours: what is it made of?   Is it silk, silver or pearls?

Maternal Love.   No, it is made of kisses and caresses and loving looks.   Each kiss you give me adds a ray of moonlight or sunshine to it.

Tyltyl.   How funny, I should never have thought that you were so rich!   Where used you to hide it?   Was it in the cupboard of which Daddy has the key?

Maternal Love.   No, no, I always wear it, but people do not see it, because people see nothing when their eyes are closed.   All mothers are rich when they love their children.   There are no poor mothers, no ugly ones, no old ones.   Their love is always the most beautiful of the Joys.   And, when they seem most sad, they need but receive or give a kiss to turn all their tears into stars in the depths of their eyes.

TYLTYL (*looking at her with astonishment*). Why, yes, it's true, your eyes are filled with stars. And they really are your eyes, only they are much more beautiful. And this is your hand too, with the little ring on it. It even has the burn which you gave it one evening when you were lighting the lamp. But it is much whiter ; and how delicate the skin is ! It's as if one saw light streaming through it. Doesn't it work like the one at the cottage ?

MATERNAL LOVE. Why, yes, it is the very same : did you never see that it becomes quite white and fills with light the moment it fondles you ?

TYLTYL. It's wonderful, Mummy : you have the same voice also ; but you speak much better than you do at home.

MATERNAL LOVE. At home, there is too much to do and there is no time. But what one does not say one hears all the same. Now that you have seen me, will you know me again, in my torn dress, when you go back to the cottage to-morrow ?

TYLTYL. I don't want to go back. Now that you are here, I want to stay also, as long as you do.

MATERNAL LOVE. But it's just the same thing : I am down below, we are all down below. You have come up here only to realize and to learn, once and for all, how to see me when you see me down below. Do you understand, Tyltyl dear ? You think yourself in Heaven ; but Heaven is wherever you and I kiss each other. There are not two mothers ; and you have no other. Every child has only one ; and it is always the same one and always the most beautiful ; but you have to know her and to know how to look. But how did you manage to come up here and to find a road which Man has been seeking ever since he began to dwell upon Earth ?

TYLTYL (*pointing to* LIGHT, *who, discreetly, has drawn a little to one side*). She brought me.

Maternal Love. Who is she ?

Tyltyl. Light.

Maternal Love. I have never seen her. I was told that she was very fond of you both and very kind. But why does she hide herself ? Does she never show her face ?

Tyltyl. Oh yes, but she is afraid that the Joys might be frightened if they saw too clearly.

Maternal Love. But doesn't she know that we are waiting only for her ! (*Calling the other* Great Joys) Come, come, sisters ! Come quickly, all of you ! Light has come to visit us at last !

(*A stir among the* Great Joys, *who draw nearer, with cries of* " Light is here ! Light ! Light ! ")

The Joy of Understanding (*thrusting all the others aside, to come and embrace* Light). You are Light and we did not know it ! And we have been waiting for you for years and years and years ! Do you know me ? I am the Joy of Understanding, who have been seeking you for so long ! We are very happy, but we do not see beyond ourselves.

The Joy of Being Just (*embracing* Light *in her turn*). Do you know me ? I am the Joy of Being Just, who have besought you so long. We are very happy, but we do not see beyond our shadows.

The Joy of Seeing what is Beautiful (*also embracing* Light). Do you know me ? I am the Joy of seeing what is Beautiful, who have loved you so dearly. We are very happy, but we do not see beyond our dreams.

The Joy of Understanding. Come, sister, come, do not keep us waiting any longer. We are strong enough, we are pure enough. Put aside those veils which still conceal from us the last truths and the last happinesses. See, all my sisters are kneeling at your feet. You are our queen and our reward.

Light (*drawing her veils closer*). Sisters, my beautiful

sisters, I am obeying my Master. The hour is not yet come ; it will strike, perhaps, and I shall return without fear and without shadow. Farewell, rise and let us kiss once more, like sisters lost and found, while waiting for the day that will soon appear.

MATERNAL LOVE (*embracing* LIGHT). You have been very good to my poor little ones.

LIGHT. I shall always be good to those who love one another.

THE JOY OF UNDERSTANDING (*going up to* LIGHT). Let the last kiss be laid upon my forehead.

(*They exchange a long kiss ; and, when they separate and raise their heads, tears are seen to stand in their eyes.*)

TYLTYL (*surprised*). Why are you crying ? (*Looking at the other* JOYS) I say ! You're crying too ! But why have all of you tears in your eyes ?

LIGHT. Hush, dear.

CURTAIN

THE KINGDOM OF THE FUTURE

ACT V

The Kingdom of the Future

*The immense halls of the Azure Palace, where the children
wait that are yet to be born. Endless perspectives of
sapphire columns supporting turquoise vaults. Everything, from the light and the lapis-lazuli flagstones to the
shimmering background into which the last arches run
and disappear, everything, down to the smallest objects,
is of an unreal, intense, fairy-like blue. Only the
plinths and capitals of the columns, the keystones, a
few seats and a few circular benches are of white marble
or alabaster. To the right, between the columns, are
great opalescent doors. These doors, which TIME will
throw back towards the end of the scene, open upon Real
Life and the quays of the Dawn. Everywhere, harmoniously peopling the hall, is a crowd of CHILDREN
robed in long azure garments. Some are playing,
others strolling to and fro, others talking or dreaming;
many are asleep, many also are working, between the
colonnades, at future inventions; and their tools,
their instruments, the apparatus which they are con-
structing, the plants, flowers and fruit which they are
cultivating or plucking are of the same supernatural and
luminous blue as the general atmosphere of the Palace.
A few tall figures, clad in a paler and more diaphanous
azure, figures of a sovereign and silent beauty, move
among the CHILDREN and would seem to be angels.*

*Enter, on the left, as though by stealth, gliding between the
columns in the foreground, TYLTYL, MYTYL and LIGHT.*

When you blow into your hands and go like this with your arms. (*He beats his arms vigorously across his chest.*)

THE CHILD. Is it cold on Earth ?

TYLTYL. Yes, sometimes, in the winter, when there is no fire.

THE CHILD. Why is there no fire ?

TYLTYL. Because it's expensive and it costs money to buy wood.

THE CHILD. What is money ?

TYLTYL. It's what you pay with.

THE CHILD. Oh !

TYLTYL. Some people have money and others have none.

THE CHILD. Why ?

TYLTYL. Because they are not rich. Are you rich ? How old are you ?

THE CHILD. I am going to be born soon. I shall be born in twelve years. Is it nice to be born ?

TYLTYL. Oh yes ! It's great fun !

THE CHILD. How did you manage ?

TYLTYL. I can't remember. It's so long ago !

THE CHILD. They say it's lovely, the Earth and the Live People !

TYLTYL. Yes, it's not bad. There are birds and cakes and toys. Some have them all ; but those who have none can look at the others.

THE CHILD. They tell us that the mothers stand waiting at the door. They are good, aren't they ?

TYLTYL. Oh yes ! They are better than anything in the world ! And the grannies too ; but they die too soon.

THE CHILD. They die ? What is that ?

TYLTYL. They go away one evening and do not come back.

THE CHILD. Why ?

TYLTYL. How can one tell ? Perhaps because they feel sad.

THE CHILD. Has yours gone ?

TYLTYL. My grandmamma?

THE CHILD. Your mamma or your grandmamma, I don't know.

TYLTYL. Oh, but it's not the same thing! The grannies go first; that's sad enough. Mine was very kind to me.

THE CHILD. What is the matter with your eyes? Are they making pearls?

TYLTYL. No; it's not pearls.

THE CHILD. What is it, then?

TYLTYL. It's nothing; it's all that blue which dazzles me a little.

THE CHILD. What is that called?

TYLTYL. What?

THE CHILD. There, that, falling down.

TYLTYL. Nothing, it's a little water.

THE CHILD. Does it come from the eyes?

TYLTYL. Yes, sometimes, when one cries.

THE CHILD. What does that mean, crying?

TYLTYL. I have not been crying; it is the fault of that blue. But, if I had cried, it would be the same thing.

THE CHILD. Does one often cry?

TYLTYL. Not little boys, but little girls do. Don't you cry here?

THE CHILD. No; I don't know how.

TYLTYL. Well, you will learn. What are you playing with, those great blue wings?

THE CHILD. These? That's for the invention which I shall make on Earth.

TYLTYL. What invention? Have you invented something?

THE CHILD. Why, yes; haven't you heard? When I am on Earth, I shall have to invent the thing that gives happiness.

TYLTYL. Is it good to eat? Does it make a noise?

THE CHILD. No, you hear nothing.

be splendid ! I shall be the gardener of the King of the Nine Planets.

Tyltyl.   The King of the Nine Planets ?   Where is he ?

The King of the Nine Planets (*advancing proudly. He looks about four years old and can hardly stand on his little crooked legs.*).   Here he is !

Tyltyl.   Well, you're not very big !

The King of the Nine Planets (*gravely and sententiously*).   I shall do such things when I am big !

Tyltyl.   What will you do ?

The King of the Nine Planets.   I shall found the General Confederation of the Solar Planets.

Tyltyl (*greatly impressed*).   Oh, really ?

The King of the Nine Planets.   They will all belong to it, except Saturn, Uranus and Neptune, which are at a preposterous and enormous distance. (*He retires with dignity.*)

Tyltyl.   I call him very interesting.

A Blue Child.   And do you see that one ?

Tyltyl.   Which one ?

The Child.   There, the little boy sleeping at the foot of the column.

Tyltyl.   What about him ?

The Child.   He will bring pure joy to the Globe.

Tyltyl.   How ?

The Child.   By means of ideas which people have not yet had.

Tyltyl.   And the other, that little fat one, with his fingers to his nose : what will he do ?

The Child.   He is to discover the fire that will warm the Earth when the Sun is paler than now.

Tyltyl.   And the two holding each other by the hand and always kissing : are they brother and sister ?

The Child.   No ; they are very comical. They are the Lovers.

Tyltyl.   What is that ?

The Child.   I don't know. Time calls them that, to

make fun of them.   They spend the day looking into each other's eyes, kissing and bidding each other farewell.

TYLTYL.   Why ?

THE CHILD.   It seems that they will not be able to leave together.

TYLTYL.   And the little pink one, who looks so serious and is sucking his thumb : what is he ?

THE CHILD.   It appears that he is to wipe out Injustice from the Earth.

TYLTYL.   Oh ?

THE CHILD.   They say it's a tremendous work.

TYLTYL.   And the little red-haired one, who walks as if he did not see where he was going.   Is he blind ?

THE CHILD.   Not yet ; but he will become so.   Look at him well ; it seems that he is to conquer Death.

TYLTYL.   What does that mean ?

THE CHILD.   I don't exactly know ; but they say it's a great thing.

TYLTYL (*pointing to a crowd of* CHILDREN *sleeping at the foot of the columns, on the steps, the benches, etc.*).   And all those asleep, what a number of them there are asleep ! Do they do nothing ?

THE CHILD.   They are thinking of something.

TYLTYL.   Of what ?

THE CHILD.   They do not know yet ; but they must take something with them to Earth : we are not allowed to go from here empty-handed.

TYLTYL.   Who says so ?

THE CHILD.   Time, who stands at the door.   You will see when he opens it.   He is very tiresome.

A CHILD (*running up from the back of the hall and elbowing his way through the crowd*).   How are you, Tyltyl ?

TYLTYL.   Hullo !   How does he know my name ?

THE CHILD (*who has just run up and who now kisses* TYLTYL *and* MYTYL *effusively*).   How are you ?   All right ? Come, give me a kiss, and you too, Mytyl.   It's not surprising that I should know your name, seeing that I shall

14

be your brother. They have only just told me that you
were here. I was right at the other end of the hall, packing
up my ideas. Tell Mummy that I am ready.

TYLTYL. What ? Are you coming to us ?

THE CHILD. Certainly, next year, on Palm Sunday.
Don't tease me too much when I am little. I am very
glad to have kissed you both beforehand. Tell Daddy to
mend the cradle. Is it comfortable in our home ?

TYLTYL. Not bad. And Mummy is so kind!

THE CHILD. And the food ?

TYLTYL. That depends. We even have cakes sometimes, don't we Mytyl ?

MYTYL. On New Year's Day and the fourteenth of
July. Mummy makes them.

TYLTYL. What have you in that bag ? Are you bringing us something ?

THE CHILD. (*very proudly*). I am bringing three ill-
nesses : scarlatina, whooping-cough and measles.

TYLTYL. Oh, as much as that ? And, afterwards,
what will you do ?

THE CHILD. Afterwards ? I shall go away.

TYLTYL. It will be hardly worth while coming !

THE CHILD. We can't pick and choose !

   (*At that moment, a sort of prolonged, powerful, crystal-
   line vibration is heard to rise and swell ; it seems
   to emanate from the columns and the opal doors,
   which are irradiated by a brighter light than before.*)

TYLTYL. What is that ?

A CHILD. That's Time ! He is going to open the
gates !

   (*A great change comes over the crowd of* BLUE CHILDREN.
   *Most of them leave their machines and their labours,
   numbers of sleepers awaken and all turn their eyes
   towards the opal doors and go nearer to them.*)

LIGHT (*joining* TYLTYL). Let us try to hide behind the columns. It will not do for Time to discover us.

TYLTYL. Where does that noise come from ?

A CHILD. It is the Dawn rising. This is the hour when the children who will be born to-day go down to earth.

TYLTYL. How will they go down ? Are there ladders ?

THE CHILD. You shall see. Time is drawing the bolts.

TYLTYL. Who is Time ?

THE CHILD. An old man who comes to call those who are going.

TYLTYL. Is he wicked ?

THE CHILD. No ; but he never listens. Beg as they may, if it's not their turn, he pushes back all those who try to go.

TYLTYL. Are they glad to leave ?

THE CHILD. We don't like being left behind, but we feel sad when we go. There ! There ! He is opening the doors !

> (*The great opalescent doors turn slowly on their hinges. The sounds of the Earth are heard like a distant music. A red and green light penetrates into the hall ;* TIME, *a tall old man with a streaming beard, armed with his scythe and hour-glass, appears upon the threshold ; and the spectator perceives the extremity of the white and gold sails of a galley moored to a sort of quay, formed by the rosy mists of the Dawn.*)

TIME (*on the threshold*). Are they ready whose hour has struck ?

BLUE CHILDREN (*elbowing their way and running up from all sides*). Here we are ! Here we are ! Here we are !

TIME (*in a gruff voice, to the* CHILDREN *defiling before him to go out*). One at a time ! Once again, there are many more of you than are wanted ! It's always the same thing ! You can't deceive me ! (*Pushing back a* CHILD) It's not your turn ! Go back and wait till to-morrow. Nor you either ; go in and return in ten years. A thirteenth shepherd ? There were only twelve wanted ; there is no use for them ; the days of Theocritus and Virgil are past. More doctors ? There are too many already ; they are grumbling about it on Earth. And where are the engineers ? They want an honest man, only one, as a phenomenon. Where is the honest man ? Is it you ? (*A* CHILD *nods yes.*) You look a very poor specimen . . . you won't have long to live ! Hallo, you, over there, not so fast, not so fast ! And you, what are you bringing ? Nothing at all, empty-handed ? Then you can't go through. Prepare something, a great crime, if you like, or a sickness, I don't care what . . . but you must have something. (*Catching sight of a little* CHILD *whom the others are pushing forward, while he resists with all his strength*) Well, what's the matter with you ? You know that the hour has come. They want a hero to fight against Injustice ; you're the one ; you must start.

THE BLUE CHILDREN. He doesn't want to, sir.

TIME. What ? He doesn't want to ? Where does the little monster think he is ? No objections, we have no time to spare.

THE CHILD (*who is being pushed*). No, no ! I don't want to go ! I would rather not be born ! I would rather stay here !

TIME. That is not the question. When the hour comes, it comes ! Now then, quick, forward !

A CHILD (*stepping forward*). Oh, let me pass ! I will go and take his place ! They say that my parents are old and have been waiting for me so long !

TIME. None of that ! You will start at your proper hour, at your proper time. We should never be done if we listened to you. One wants to go, another refuses ; it's too soon or it's too late. (*Pushing back some* CHIL-

TIME OPENS THE GATES OF DAWN

DREN *who have encroached upon the threshold*) Not so
near, you children! Back, you inquisitive ones! Those
who are not starting have no business outside. You are
in a hurry now; later, when your turn comes, you will
be frightened and hang back. Look, there are four who
are trembling like leaves. (*To a* CHILD *who, on the point
of crossing the threshold, suddenly goes back*) Well, what
is it? What's the matter?

THE CHILD. I have forgotten the box containing the
two crimes which I shall have to commit.

ANOTHER CHILD. And I the little pot with my idea
for enlightening the crowd.

A THIRD CHILD. I have forgotten the graft of my
finest pear.

TIME. Run quick and fetch them! We have only
six hundred and twelve seconds left. The galley of the
Dawn is flapping her sails to show that she is waiting.
You will come too late and you won't be born! Come,
quick, on board with you! (*Laying hold of a* CHILD *who
tries to pass between his legs to reach the quay*) Oh, no,
not you! This is the third time you've tried to be born
before your turn. Don't let me catch you at it again,
or you can wait for ever with my sister Eternity; and
you know that it's not amusing there! But come,
are we ready? Is every one at his post? (*Surveying the*
CHILDREN *standing on the quay or already seated in the
galley*) There is still one missing. It is no use his hiding,
I see him in the crowd. You can't deceive me! Come on,
you, the little fellow whom they call the Lover, say good-
bye to your sweetheart.

>(*The two* CHILDREN *who are called the Lovers, fondly
entwined, their faces livid with despair, go up to*
TIME *and kneel at his feet.*)

THE FIRST CHILD. Mr. Time, let me stay behind with
her!

THE SECOND CHILD. Mr. Time, let me go with him !

TIME. Impossible ! We have only three hundred and ninety-four seconds left.

THE FIRST CHILD. I would rather not be born !

TIME. You cannot choose.

THE SECOND CHILD (*beseechingly*). Mr. Time, I shall come too late !

THE FIRST CHILD. I shall be gone before she comes down !

THE SECOND CHILD. I shall never see him again !

THE FIRST CHILD. We shall be alone in the world !

TIME. All this does not concern me. Address your entreaties to Life. I unite and part as I am told. (*Seizing one of the* CHILDREN) Come !

THE FIRST CHILD (*struggling*). No, no, no ! She too !

THE SECOND CHILD (*clinging to the clothes of the* FIRST). Leave him with me ! Leave him !

TIME. Come, come, he is not going to die, but to live ! (*Dragging away the* FIRST CHILD) Come along.

THE SECOND CHILD (*stretching her arms out frantically to the* CHILD *that is being carried off*). A sign ! A sign ! Tell me how to find you !

THE FIRST CHILD. I shall always love you !

THE SECOND CHILD. I shall be the saddest thing on earth ! You will know me by that ! (*She falls and remains stretched on the ground.*)

TIME. You would do much better to hope. And now, that is all. (*Consulting his hour-glass*) We have only sixty-three seconds left.

> (*Last and violent movements among the* CHILDREN *departing and remaining. They exchange hurried farewells.*)

THE BLUE CHILDREN. Good-bye, Pierre ! Good-bye Jean ! Have you all you want ? Announce my idea ! Have you forgotten nothing ? Try to know me again !

THE FAREWELL OF THE LOVERS

I shall find you ! Don't lose your ideas ! Don't lean too far into Space ! Send me your news ! They say one can't ! Yes, you can, if you try ! Try to let us know if it's nice ! I will come to meet you ! I shall be born on a throne !

TIME (*shaking his keys and his scythe*). Enough ! Enough ! The anchor's weighed !

> (*The sails of the galley pass and disappear. The voices of the* CHILDREN *in the galley are heard in the distance:* " Earth ! Earth ! I see it ! How beautiful it is ! How bright it is ! How big it is ! " *Then, as though issuing from the depths of the abyss, an extremely distant song of gladness and expectation.*)

TYLTYL (*to* LIGHT). What is that ? It is not they singing. It sounds like other voices.

LIGHT. Yes, it is the song of the mothers coming out to meet them.

> (*Meanwhile,* TIME *closes the opalescent doors. He turns to take a last look at the hall and suddenly perceives* TYLTYL, MYTYL *and* LIGHT.)

TIME (*dumbfoundered and furious*). What's that ? What are you doing here ? Who are you ? Why are you not blue ? How did you get in ? (*He comes forward threatening them with his scythe.*)

LIGHT (*to* TYLTYL). Do not answer ! I have the Blue Bird. He is hidden under my cloak. Let us escape. Turn the diamond, he will lose our traces.

> (*They slip away on the left, between the columns in the foreground.*)

CURTAIN

ACT VI

SCENE I. *The Leave-taking*

The stage represents a wall with a small door. It is break of day.

Enter TYLTYL, MYTYL, LIGHT, BREAD, WATER, SUGAR, FIRE *and* MILK.

LIGHT.   You would never guess where we are.

TYLTYL.   Well, no, Light, because I don't know.

LIGHT.   Don't you recognize that wall and that little door ?

TYLTYL.   I see a red wall and a little green door.

LIGHT.   And doesn't that remind you of anything ?

TYLTYL.   It reminds me that Time showed us the door.

LIGHT.   How odd people are when they dream ! They do not recognize their own hands.

TYLTYL.   Who is dreaming ? Am I ?

LIGHT.   Perhaps it's myself. Who can tell ? However, this wall contains a house which you have seen more than once since you were born.

TYLTYL.   A house which I have seen more than once ?

LIGHT.   Why yes, sleepy-head ! It is the house which we left one evening, just a year ago, to a day.

TYLTYL.   Just a year ago ? Why, then . . .

LIGHT.   Don't open great eyes like sapphire caves. It's the dear old house of your father and mother.

TYLTYL (*going up to the door*).   But I think . . . Yes, really . . . It seems to me . . . This little door . . . I recognize the wooden pin. Are they in there ? Are we

108

near Mummy ?   I want to go in at once.   I want to kiss her at once !

LIGHT.   One moment.   They are sound asleep ; you must not wake them with a start.   Besides, the door will not open till the hour strikes.

TYLTYL.   What hour ?   Is there long to wait ?

LIGHT.   Alas, no !   A few poor minutes.

TYLTYL.   Aren't you glad to be back ?   What is it, Light ?   You are quite pale, you look ill.

LIGHT.   It's nothing, child.   I feel a little sad, because I am leaving you.

TYLTYL.   Leaving us ?

LIGHT.   I must.   I have nothing more to do here ; the year is over, the Fairy is coming back to ask you for the Blue Bird.

TYLTYL.   But I haven't got the Blue Bird !   The one of the Land of Memory turned quite black, the one of the Future turned quite red, Night's are dead and I could not catch the one in the Forest.   Is it my fault if they change colour, or die, or escape ?   Will the Fairy be angry and what will she say ?

LIGHT.   We have done what we could.   It seems likely that the Blue Bird does not exist or that he changes colour when he is caged.

TYLTYL.   Where is the cage ?

BREAD.   Here, master.   It was entrusted to my diligent care during that long and parlous journey ; to-day, now that my mission is drawing to an end, I restore it to your hands, untouched and carefully closed, as I received it. (*Like an orator making a speech*) And now, in the name of all, I crave permission to add a few words . . .

FIRE.   He has not been called upon to speak !

WATER.   Order !

BREAD.   The malevolent interruptions of a contemptible enemy, of an envious rival . . . (*raising his voice*) will not prevent me from doing my duty to the end.   I wish, therefore, in the name of all . . .

15

Dog, *who overwhelms her with bites, blows and kicks.*)

The Dog (*beating the* Cat). There! Have you had enough? Do you want any more? There! There! There!

Light, Tyltyl *and* Mytyl (*rushing forward to part them*). Tylô! Are you mad? Well, I never! Down! Stop that, will you? How dare you? Wait, wait!

(*They part the* Dog *and the* Cat *by main force.*)

Light. What is it. What has happened?

The Cat (*blubbering and wiping her eyes*). It's the Dog, Mrs. Light. He insulted me, he put tin-tacks in my food, he pulled my tail, he beat me; and I had done nothing, nothing, nothing at all!

The Dog (*mimicking her*). Nothing, nothing, nothing at all! (*In an undertone, with a mocking grimace*) Never mind, you've had some, you've had some and you're going to have some more!

Mytyl (*pressing the* Cat *in her arms*). My poor Tylette, where has he hurt you? Tell me. You'll make me cry too.

Light (*to the* Dog, *severely*). Your conduct is all the more unworthy since you have chosen for this disgraceful exhibition the already most painful moment when we are about to part from these poor children.

The Dog (*suddenly sobered*). To part from these poor children?

Light. Yes, the hour which you know of is at hand. We are going to return to Silence. We shall no longer be able to speak to them.

The Dog (*suddenly uttering real howls of despair and flinging himself upon the* Children, *whom he loads with violent and tumultuous caresses*). No! No! I refuse! I refuse! I shall always talk! You will understand me

now, will you not, my little god ? Yes ! Yes ! Yes ! And
we shall tell each other everything, everything, everything !
And I shall be very good. And I shall learn to read and
write and play dominoes ! And I shall always be very
clean. And I shall never steal anything in the kitchen
again. Shall I do a wonderful trick for you ? Would
you like to see me kiss the Cat ?

MYTYL (*to the* CAT). And you, Tylette ? Have you
nothing to say to us ?

THE CAT (*in an affected and mysterious tone*). I love
you both, as much as you deserve.

LIGHT. Now let me, in my turn, children, give you a
last kiss.

TYLTYL *and* MYTYL (*hanging on to* LIGHT'S *dress*). No,
no, no, Light ! Stay here with us ! Daddy won't mind.
We will tell Mummy how kind you have been.

LIGHT. Alas, I cannot ! This door is closed to us and
I must leave you.

TYLTYL. Where will you go all alone ?

LIGHT. Not very far, my children ; over there, to
the Land of the Silence of Things.

TYLTYL. No, no ; I won't have you go. We will
go with you. I shall tell Mummy.

LIGHT. Do not cry, my dear little ones. I have not a
voice like Water ; I have only my brightness, which Man
does not understand. But I watch over him to the end
of his days. Never forget that I am speaking to you in
every spreading moonbeam, in every twinkling star, in
every dawn that rises, in every lamp that is lit, in every
good and bright thought of your soul. (*Eight o'clock
strikes behind the wall.*) Listen ! The hour is striking !
Good-bye ! The door is opening ! In with you, in with
you !

    (*She pushes the* CHILDREN *through the door, which
       has half-opened and which closes again behind
       them.* BREAD *wipes away a furtive tear*, SUGAR

and WATER, *all in tears, and the others flee pre-*
cipitously and disappear in the wings to the right
and left. The DOG *howls behind the scenes.*
The stage remains empty for a moment and then
the scenery representing the wall and the little
door opens in the middle and reveals the last scene.)

SCENE II.   *The Awakening*

The same setting as in ACT I, *but the objects, the walls and*
the atmosphere all appear incomparably and magically
fresher, happier, more smiling. The daylight penetrates
gaily through the chinks of the closed shutters. To the
right, at the back, TYLTYL *and* MYTYL *lie sound asleep*
in their two little beds. The DOG, *the* CAT *and the*
THINGS are in the places which they occupied in ACT I,
before the arrival of the FAIRY.

Enter MUMMY TYL.

MUMMY TYL (*in a cheerfully scolding voice*).   Up, come,
get up, you little lazybones! Aren't you ashamed of
yourselves?   It has struck eight and the sun is high
above the trees! Lord, how they sleep, how they sleep!
(*She stoops and kisses the* CHILDREN.)   They are quite
rosy.   Tyltyl smells of lavender and Mytyl of lilies-of-
the-valley. (*Kissing them again*) What sweet things
children are!   Still, they can't go on sleeping till midday.
I mustn't let them grow up idle. And, besides, I have
heard that it's not very healthy. (*Gently shaking* TYLTYL)
Wake up, wake up, Tyltyl.
  TYLTYL (*waking up*).   What? Light? Where is she?
No, no, don't go away.
  MUMMY TYL.   Light? Why, of course it's light. Has

THE BIRD ABOUT TO FLY OFF BETWEEN THE CHILDREN'S HANDS

been for ever so long.   It's as bright as noonday, though the shutters are closed.   Wait a bit till I open them. (*She throws back the shutters and the dazzling daylight invades the room.*)   There!   See!   What's the matter with you?   You look quite blinded.

TYLTYL (*rubbing his eyes*).   Mummy, Mummy!   It's you!

MUMMY TYL.   Why, of course, it's I.   Who did you think it was?

TYLTYL.   It's you.   Yes, yes, it's you!

MUMMY TYL.   Yes, yes, it's I.   I haven't changed my face since last night.   Why do you stare at me in that wonderstruck way?   Is my nose turned upside down, by any chance?

TYLTYL.   Oh, how nice it is to see you again!   It's so long, so long ago!   I must kiss you at once.   Again! Again!   Again!   And this is my own bed!   I am at home!

MUMMY TYL.   What's the matter?   Why don't you wake up?   Don't tell me you're ill!   Let me see, show me your tongue.   Come, get up and dress.

TYLTYL.   Hullo, I'm in my shirt!

MUMMY TYL.   Why, of course you are!   Put on your breeches and your little jacket.   There they are, on the chair.

TYLTYL.   Was I like this all through the journey?

MUMMY TYL.   What journey?

TYLTYL.   Why, last year.

MUMMY TYL.   Last year?

TYLTYL.   Why, yes!   At Christmas, when I went away.

MUMMY TYL.   When you went away?   You haven't left the room.   I put you to bed last night; and here you are this morning.   Have you been dreaming all that?

TYLTYL.   But you don't understand!   It was last year, when I went away with Mytyl, the Fairy, Light— how nice Light is!—Bread, Sugar, Water, Fire.   They were fighting all the time!   You're not angry with me?

Did you feel very sad ?   And what did Daddy say ?   I
could not refuse.   I left a note to explain.

MUMMY TYL.   What are you talking about ?   For sure,
either you're ill or else you're still asleep.   (*She gives him
a friendly shake.*)   There, wake up.   There, is that
better ?

TYLTYL.   But, Mummy, I assure you . . . It's you that
are still asleep.

MUMMY TYL.   What !   Still asleep, am I ?   Why, I've
been up since six o'clock !   I've finished all the cleaning
and lit the fire.

TYLTYL.   But ask Mytyl if it's not true.   Oh, we've
had such adventures !

MUMMY TYL.   Why, Mytyl ?   What do you mean ?

TYLTYL.   She was with me.   We saw Grandad and
Granny.

MUMMY TYL (*more and more bewildered*).   Grandad and
Granny ?

TYLTYL.   Yes, in the Land of Memory.   It was on our
way.   They are dead, but they are quite well.   Granny
made us a lovely plum-tart.   And then the little brothers
Robert, Jean, with his top ; and Madeleine and Pierrette ;
and Pauline ; and Riquette too.

MYTYL.   Riquette still goes about on all fours !

TYLTYL.   And Pauline still has a pimple on her nose.

MYTYL.   We saw you too, last night.

MUMMY TYL.   Last night ?   No wonder, as I put you
to bed.

TYLTYL.   No, no, in the Gardens of Happiness.   You
were much prettier, but you were like, all the same.

MUMMY TYL.   The Gardens of Happiness ?   I don't
know what you mean.

TYLTYL (*looking at her and then kissing her*).   Yes, you
were prettier, but I like you better as you are.

MYTYL (*also kissing her*).   So do I, so do I.

MUMMY TYL (*touched, but very anxious*).   Dear heaven !
What's the matter with them ?   I shall lose them too, as

I lost the others! (*Suddenly mad with alarm, she calls out*) Daddy Tyl! Come, quick! The children are ill!

> *Enter* Daddy Tyl, *very calmly, with an axe in his hand.*

Daddy Tyl.   What is it?

Tyltyl *and* Mytyl (*running up gaily to kiss their father*). Hullo, Daddy! It's Daddy! Good morning, Daddy! Have you had plenty of work this year?

Daddy Tyl.   Well, what's the matter? They don't look ill; they look very well.

Mummy Tyl (*sobbing*).   You can't trust their looks. It will be as with the others. They looked quite well also to the end; and then God took them. I don't know what's the matter with them. I put them to bed quite quietly last night; and this morning, when they woke up, everything was wrong. They don't know what they're saying; they talk about a journey. They have seen Light and Grandad and Granny, who are dead, but who are quite well.

Tyltyl.   But Grandad still has his wooden leg.

Mytyl.   And Granny her rheumatics.

Mummy Tyl.   Do you hear? Run and fetch the doctor!

Daddy Tyl.   Why, no, no. They are not dead yet. Come, let us look into this. (*A knock at the front door.*) Come in!

> *Enter* Neighbour Berlingot, *a little old woman resembling the* Fairy *in* Act I *and leaning on a stick.*

The Neighbour.   Good-morning and a Merry Christmas to you all!

Tyltyl.   It's the Fairy Bérylune!

The Neighbour.   I have come to ask for a bit of fire

for my Christmas stew.   It's very chilly this morning. Good-morning, children, how are you ?

TYLTYL.   Fairy Bérylune, I could not find the Blue Bird.

THE NEIGHBOUR.   What is he saying ?

MUMMY TYL.   Don't ask me, Madame Berlingot.   They don't know what they are saying.   They have been like that since they woke up.   They must have eaten something that disagreed with them.

THE NEIGHBOUR.   Why, Tyltyl, don't you remember Goody Berlingot, your Neighbour Berlingot ?

TYLTYL.   Why, yes, ma'am.   You are the Fairy Bérylune.   You're not angry with us ?

THE NEIGHBOUR.   Béry . . . what ?

TYLTYL.   Bérylune.

THE NEIGHBOUR.   Berlingot, you mean Berlingot.

TYLTYL.   Bérylune or Berlingot, as you please, ma'am. But Mytyl knows.

MUMMY TYL.   That's the worst of it, that Mytyl also. . . . .

DADDY TYL.   Pooh, pooh !   That will soon go ; I will give them a smack or two.

THE NEIGHBOUR.   Don't ; it's not worth while.   I know the sort of thing : it's only a little fit of dreaming. They must have been sleeping in the moonbeams.   My little girl, who is very ill, is often like that.

MUMMY TYL.   By the way, how is your little girl ?

THE NEIGHBOUR.   Only so-so.   She can't get up. The doctor says that it's her nerves.   I know what would cure her for all that.   She was asking me for it only this morning, for her Christmas box ; it's a notion she has.

MUMMY TYL.   Yes, I know ; it 's Tyltyl's bird.   Well, Tyltyl, aren't you going to give it to the poor little thing at last ?

TYLTYL.   What, Mummy ?

MUMMY TYL.   Your bird.   He's no use to you.   You never even look at him now.   And she has been dying to have him for ever so long !

THE CHILDREN RECOUNT THEIR ADVENTURES

Tyltyl. Hullo, that's true, my bird ! Where is he ?
Oh, there's the cage ! Mytyl, do you see the cage ? It's
the one which Bread carried. Yes, yes, it's the same one,
but there's only one bird in it. Has he eaten the other,
I wonder ? Think of that ! Hullo, he's blue ! Why,
it's my dove ! But he's much bluer than when I went
away ! Why, that's the Blue Bird we were looking for !
We went so far and he was here all the time ! Oh, but
that's wonderful ! Mytyl, do you see the bird ? What
would Light say ? I will take down the cage. (*He
climbs on a chair, takes down the cage and carries it to the*
Neighbour.) There, Madame Berlingot, there you are.
He's not quite blue yet, but that will come, you shall see !
Take him quickly to your little girl.

The Neighbour. Really ? Do you mean it ? Do
you give it me just like that, straight away and for nothing ?
Lord, how happy she will be ! (*Kissing* Tyltyl) I must
give you a kiss ! I fly ! I fly !

Tyltyl. Yes, yes ; be quick. Some of them change
their colour.

The Neighbour. I will come back to tell you what
she says.

(*She goes out.*)

Tyltyl (*after taking a long look around him*). Daddy,
Mummy, what have you done to the house ? It's just
as it was, but it's much prettier.

Daddy Tyl. How do you mean, it's prettier ?

Tyltyl. Why, yes, everything has been painted and
made to look new, everything is clean and polished. It
was not like that last year.

Daddy Tyl. Last year ?

Tyltyl (*going to the window*). And look at the forest !
How big and fine it is ! One would think it was new !
How happy I feel here ! (*Going to the bread-pan and
opening it*) Where's Bread ? I say, the loaves are very
quiet. And then here's Tylô ! Hullo, Tylô, Tylô !

Ah, you had a fine fight! Do you remember, in the forest?

Mytyl. And Tylette. She knows me, but she doesn't talk.

Tyltyl. Mr. Bread. (*Feeling his forehead*) Hullo, the diamond's gone! Who's taken my little green hat? Never mind; I don't want it now. Ah, Fire! He's a good one! He crackles, for fun, to make Water angry. (*Running to the tap*) And Water? Good-morning, Water! What does she say? She still talks, but I don't understand her as well as I did.

Mytyl. I don't see Sugar.

Tyltyl. Lord, how happy I am, happy, happy, happy!

Mytyl. So am I, so am I!

Mummy Tyl. What are you spinning round for like that?

Daddy Tyl. Don't mind them and don't distress yourself. They are playing at being happy.

Tyltyl. I liked Light best of all. Where's her lamp? Can we light it? (*Looking round him again*) Goodness me, how lovely it all is and how glad I feel!

(*A knock at the front door.*)

Daddy Tyl. Come in, come in!

> Enter the Neighbour, *holding by the hand a fair-haired* Little Girl *of wondrous beauty, who carries* Tyltyl's *dove pressed in her arms.*

The Neighbour. Do you see the miracle?

Mummy Tyl. Impossible! Can she walk?

The Neighbour. Can she walk? She can run, she can dance, she can fly! When she saw the bird, she jumped just like that, with one bound, to the window, to see by the light if it was really Tyltyl's dove. And then, whoosh!

Out into the street, like an angel! It was as much as I could do to keep pace with her.

Tyltyl (*going up to her, wonderstruck*). Oh, how like Light she is!

Mytyl. She is much smaller.

Tyltyl. Yes, indeed! But she will grow bigger.

The Neighbour. What are they saying? Haven't they got over it yet?

Mummy Tyl. They are better, they are mending. It will be all right when they have had their breakfasts.

The Neighbour (*pushing the* Little Girl *into* Tyltyl's *arms*). Come along, child, come and thank Tyltyl.

(Tyltyl, *suddenly bashful, takes a step back.*)

Mummy Tyl. Well, Tyltyl, what's the matter? Are you afraid of the little girl? Come, give her a kiss, a good big kiss. No, a better one than that. You're not so shy as a rule! Another one! But what's the matter with you? You look as if you were going to cry.

(Tyltyl, *after kissing the* Little Girl *rather awkwardly, stands in front of her for a moment; and the two children look at each other without speaking. Then* Tyltyl *strokes the dove's head.*)

Tyltyl. Is he blue enough?

The Little Girl. Yes, I am so pleased with him.

Tyltyl. I have seen bluer ones. But those which are quite blue, you know, do what you will, you can't catch them.

The Little Girl. That doesn't matter; he's lovely.

Tyltyl. Has he had anything to eat?

The Little Girl. Not yet. What does he eat?

Tyltyl. Anything: corn, bread, Indian corn, grasshoppers.

The Little Girl. I say, how does he eat?

PRINTED BY
JARROLD AND SONS LTD.
NORWICH